a crack in the rear-view mirror

A VIEW OF INDUSTRIALIZED BUILDING

a crack in the rear-view mirror

A VIEW OF INDUSTRIALIZED BUILDING

RICHARD BENDER

EDITED AND ILLUSTRATED BY FORREST WILSON

FOREWORD BY EZRA EHRENKRANTZ

VNR **VAN NOSTRAND REINHOLD COMPANY**
New York • Cincinnati • Toronto • London • Melbourne

Van Nostrand Reinhold Company Regional Offices:
New York Cincinnati Chicago Millbrae Dallas

Van Nostrand Reinhold Company International Offices:
London Toronto Melbourne

Manufactured in the United States of America
Published by Van Nostrand Reinhold Company
450 West 33rd Street, New York, N.Y. 10001

Published simultaneously in Canada by Van Nostrand
Reinhold Ltd.

15 14 13 12 11 10 9 8 7 6 5 4 3 2 1

Library of Congress Cataloging in Publication Data

Bender, Richard, 1930-
    A crack in the rear view mirror.

    Includes bibliographical references.
    1. Industrialized building. I. Title.
TH1000.B45   694.9'7   72-12908

acknowledgments

**For my father
Edward Bender
who did more than he
or I realized**

This work began with a technical
assignment from the National Commission on Urban Problems, in 1967,
and was developed over the years
with the help of many friends—
students, colleagues, and clients. It
owes more than I can describe to all
the students who listened, questioned,
and added to my understanding.

Most of all, it owes a great deal to
Forrest Wilson. Beyond editing and
illustrating the book, his spirit drew
me into writing and kept me at it.

RICHARD BENDER
Amangansett, N. Y.

foreword

Our current building vocabulary has come down to us from Elizabethan times. When houses were constructed of brick, the backs of fireplaces in the low-income houses of the day were two bricks wide or 18". Bricks were sized to a man's hand span of 4½" and they were 9" long so that one could bond a wall. Firewood was cut to 16" lengths so that it would fit into the fireplace and when the wood-lath tradition of the Elizabethan era came into vogue, the lath was cut from the firewood. This 16" module permeates much of our construction today at the same time that the 9" brick module is reflected in our floor tile and related products.

It is easy to decry the slow rate of evolution within the building industry and, at the same time, to become excited about such new technologies as membrane structures, the use of plastics, and the recycling of water. Although the future looks so bright and exciting, in view of the slow rate of progress which seems to be an embedded tradition of the industry, we may well ask, "How do we get from here to there?" This book pinpoints the direction the industry is taking, not through a violent revolution but through an accumulation of many small and perhaps unglamorous steps.

The flow of progress is, at last, beginning to provide significant pressure against the walls which have resisted or slowed change in the past. While we know that the 300 years of battle that has been waged within the building industry between the adherents of the brick module and those of the firewood, the direction which the industry will take in the future still remains very much in doubt. Will our built environment be manufactured by General Motors and sold by Madison Avenue or will it provide for wider ranging and more responsive human requirements? Who will determine what the new forms should be? The fact is, that the changes are inevitable but they can only be guided by an aware and interested community.

This book presents, for the first time, the evidence that the industry *is* changing rapidly, in spite of the fact that some of the more illustrious attempts at industrialization have not succeeded. The buildup of information on materials, methods, and techniques as indicated in this book represents a virtual information explosion. The compilation ranges from the development of new materials, to the development of processes, and the related organizational structures to deliver these processes. There is, in fact, an explosion of new developments of building systems and products. Many drop by the wayside, but the accumulation of gains persists. The failures have, perhaps, masked the real nature of progress. Let us hope that Richard Bender's book makes us aware of the need to exercise our rights to determine future choice as this need becomes more immediate and pressing.

EZRA D. EHRENKRANTZ, *A.I.A.*

a crack in the rear-view mirror

A VIEW OF INDUSTRIALIZED BUILDING

prologue:
new forces

"Technical change has been primarily evolutionary, in small increments, significant only in the aggregate. But there has been a wave of change, so diffuse and made up of so many small parts that it can hardly be called an innovation in the usual sense at all. It might better be called the industrialization of building."
—Donald Schon
from *Technology and Change*

Schon puts it clearly: industrialization has crept into building. There has been no sudden change, no single invention, or technical innovation which can be pointed to as industrializing building, but certainly the industry today has a very different look from that of a generation ago. For those whose picture of modern production is the auto assembly line, building seems far from industrialized. But perhaps it is just this view of industrialization (as only machinery, tools, production lines, and automation) that has been standing in the way of significant advances. Perhaps our focus on what has been is standing in the way of our recognizing significant changes in the industry itself and bringing about significant changes in the building process.

Photo courtesy of Chevrolet Motor Company.

1

proceedings held at the castle of york, january 1813

The Luddites*

The trial of the Luddites coined a word for opposition to mechanization. The words of the judge, Mr. Baron Thomson, have a familiar ring.

". . . Those mischievous Associations, dangerous to the public peace, as well as destructive of the property of individual subjects, and in some instances of their lives, seem to have originated in a neighbouring country, and at first to have had for their object merely the destruction of machinery invented for the purpose of saving manual labour in manufactures: a notion, probably suggested by evil designing persons, to captivate the working manufacturer, and engage him in tumult and crimes, by persuading him that the use of machinery occasions a decrease of the demand for personal labour, and a consequent decrease of wages, or total want of work. A more fallacious and unfounded argument cannot be made use of. It is to the excellence of our Machinery that the existence probably, certainly the excellence and flourishing state, of our manufactures are owing. Whatever diminishes expense, increases consumption, and the demand for the article both in the home and foreign market; and were the use of machinery entirely to be abolished, the cessation of the manufacture itself would soon follow, inasmuch as other countries, to which the machinery would be banished, would be enabled to undersell us. . . ."

An Introduction to Contemporary Civilization in the West, **3rd edition, New York, Columbia University Press, 1961, pp. 254-261.**

Crane setting first module of 3-home Levitt townhouse.

Photo courtesy of Chevrolet Motor Company.

the machines
by Samuel Butler*

In Erewhon, the story of a mythical land which has banned all machines, Samuel Butler expresses a 19th cenutry fear of mechanization.

" . . . True, from a low materialistic point of view, it would seem that those thrive best who use machinery wherever its use is possible with profit; but this is the art of the machines—they serve that they may rule."

". . . The machines being of themselves unable to struggle, have got man to do their struggling for them: as long as he fulfills this function duly, all goes well with him—at least he thinks so; but the moment he fails to do his best for the advancement of machinery by encouraging the good and destroying the bad, he is left behind in the race of competition; and this means that he will be made uncomfortable in a variety of ways, and perhaps die.

". . . It is said by some with whom I have conversed upon this subject, that the machines can never be developed into animate or quasi-animate existences, inasmuch as they have no reproductive system, nor seem ever likely to possess one. If this be taken to mean that they cannot marry, and that we are never likely to see a fertile union between two vapour-engines with young ones playing about the door of the shed, however greatly we might desire to do so, I will readily grant it. But the objection is not a very profound one. No one expects that all the features of the now existing organisations will be absolutely repeated in an entirely new class of life. The reproductive system of animals differs widely from that of plants, but both are reproductive systems. Has nature exhausted her phases of this power?

"Surely if a machine is able to reproduce another machine systematically, we may say that it has a reproductive system. What is a reproductive system, if it be not a system for reproduction? And how few of the machines are there which have not been produced systematically by other machines? But it is man that makes them do so. Yes; but is it not insects that make many of the plants reproductive, and would not whole families of plants die out if their fertilisation was not effected by a class of agents utterly foreign to themselves? Does any one say that the red clover has no reproductive system because the bumble bee (and the bumble bee only) must aid and abet it before it can reproduce? No one. The bumble bee is a part of the reproductive system of the clover. Each one of ourselves has sprung from minute animalcules whose entity was entirely distinct from our own, and which acted after their kind with no thought or heed of what we might think about it. These little creatures are part of our own reproductive system; then why are not we part of that of the machines?

"But the machines which reproduce machinery do not reproduce machines after their own kind. A thimble may be made by machinery, but it was not made by, neither will it ever make, a thimble. Here, again, if we turn to nature we shall find abundance of analogies which will teach us that a reproductive system may be in full force without the thing produced being of the same kind as that which produced it. Very few creatures reproduce after their own kind: they reproduce something which has the potentiality of becoming that which their parents were. Thus the butterfly lays an egg, which egg can become a caterpillar, which caterpillar can become a chrysalis, which crysalis can become a butterfly; and though I freely grant that the machines cannot be said to have more than the germ of a true reproductive system at present, have we not just seen that they have only recently obtained the germs of a mouth and stomach? And may not some stride be made in the direction of true reproduction which shall be as great as that which has been recently taken in the direction of true feeding?"

*In Erewhon: or Over the Range, 1st Edition, 1872

introduction

Building today is dominated by change—changing techniques, organizations, and attitudes. We give many names to this change: industrialization, systems building, prefabrication, rationalization, and others which reflect our various points of view. A careful study of the building industry will reveal a change from traditionally accepted practices to new methods which involve analysis, research, development, manufacturing, and marketing.

It is not surprising that this situation breeds confusion. These changes affect our methods of dealing with problems and the problems themselves. They affect the roles we play within the context of change. We are actors trying to learn parts in a play which is yet to be written.

With this in mind, this book will not attempt a broad survey of industrialized building. It is too late—or too early—for that. Several years ago such a survey could have been a complete and useful reference. Indeed some of the material for this book is based on a study of the State of the Art of Industrialized Building, prepared for the National Commission on Urban Problems in 1968. At that time there was a discrete body of work emerging in sharp contrast to conventional building. The early surveys of industrialization were thin volumes, but through the years they have become increasingly larger. Annual supplements are now required to keep up with the explosion of new material. Periodicals which once treated the industrialization of building in occasional articles now devote entire issues to the subject. New periodicals are devoted to industrialized building alone. It seems the only activity outstripping the move to industrialize building is the flood of written material describing it. Scattered participation by industry has strengthened and expanded. Less than twenty groups were prepared to make serious proposals for the HUD "In-Cities R and D Program" in 1968.

A year later, over 1500 company representatives attended the "Operation Breakthrough" bidders meeting; more than 600 proposals were received. Over 250 consortiums submitted full system bids in the final Breakthrough competition. Sheer volume alone makes the task of a comprehensive survey impossible.*

However what is appropriate and extremely important at this point is a clarification. What is industrialized building? What are its methods, organizations, attitudes, and its future? We will examine these questions and use this examination as the basis for the projection of three scenarios: each an alternate future for building.

*A bibliography is included to give the reader the means to survey and keep abreast of this information.

change

Hundreds of millions of people around the world, looking for a better life, now expect, and are demanding, a reshaping of the environment toward their needs, desires, and requirements.

An increasing number of those of us involved in building realize that our approach is at least partially responsible for our failure to meet these demands. Many of us blame the industrial process for the chaotic environment we live in, rather than placing the blame where it belongs: on men and institutions who have not learned to control it.

Why is it that, in the age of electronic computers, space travel, and the mass production of every kind of commodity, we are just beginning the industrialization of the building process? How can such a major sector of the world's economy be so retarded that only recently has the industrialization of building been considered a subject for serious discussion?

Most major industries have passed through industrialization. Many are now approaching the state of automation. What is so exceptional about building?

The production of buildings is one of the most complex and difficult of all operations. To assemble the land, money, labor, materials, and equipment necessary to build even a small house is a process which is proportionately more involved than that of building an ocean liner. Hundreds of separate items made by different manufacturers and distributed through various channels are individually assembled from a host of sources. The talents of a whole hierarchy of skilled trades and professions must be dovetailed. A network of building and zoning ordinances, often contradictory and nearly always obsolete, have to be negotiated, as do all the legal processes involving transfer of land titles, ownership, and financing. As a result of this complex, archaic system, building prices are high, quality low, and output inadequate.

From a technological point of view it is clear that building construction can be better adapted to the social conditions of our day as well as to contemporary means of production: factories, tools, research, and organization.

New techniques and materials allow us to do almost limitless things. We can produce structures of incredible height, control climate, and support buildings with air. We can do this with a bewildering choice of methods and materials. Paradoxically it is this bewildering network of interrelated choices and techniques that makes much of today's building chaotic. It is appalling that, at a time when production is potentially sufficient to supply the necessities of life to every man, woman, and child in the world, millions of people are homeless.

Much of the answer to this dilemma is to be found in a statement of Henry Ford:

"The term mass production is used to describe the modern method by which great quantities of a single standardized commodity are manufactured. Mass production is not merely quantity production . . . nor is it merely machine production. Mass production is the focusing upon a manufacturing project of the principles of power, accuracy, economy, system, continuity, and speed. The interpretation of these principles, through studies of operation and machine development and their coordination, is the conspicuous task of management. And the normal result is a productive organization that delivers in quantities a useful commodity of standard material, workmanship, and design at a minimum cost . . ."

We have focused on "quantity" and the "machine" before we have developed the framework Ford describes. We have been trying to find "how to build" before we know "what to build." We have rushed ahead to turn new technology to the production of obsolete forms, using jet-age technology to produce horse-and-buggy houses.

Photo courtesy of General Electric Company.

Photo courtesy of Western Wood Products Association.

Photo courtesy of Volkswagon.

Photo courtesy of The Port of New York Authority.

Photo courtesy of Expo Corporation.

Multipurpose sports arena. (Photo courtesy of Owens Corning Fiberglass.)

Photo by Forrest Wilson.

Photo courtesy of Automated Building Components, Inc.

We tend to mistake the superficial trappings of industrialization for the real thing while we continue to ignore the new forces, forms, and tools of the industrial age.

Marshall McLuhan made it clear that: ". . . each new medium uses an earlier medium as content . . ." In this way, the printing presses took over stories developed from the spoken word, the moving picture took material from books, television uses movies as content, and industrialized housing has taken the Victorian house as its model.

Our most advanced technologies, organization, tools, automation, control systems, planning, design and research are focused on making obsolete houses faster and cheaper. Yet we can not take full advantage of our new technologies until both product and process are changed, until both are understood and attuned to each other.

The printed circuit is a good example of the way another industry faced this challenge.

After World War II, the electronics industry was faced with an exploding demand for the production of electronic circuitry for radio, television, and electronic computers. It could not meet the demand with conventional methods. Costs soared while quality fell. Many attempts were made to develop new machinery to wire circuits, but the precision, delicacy, and complexity of these materials made the machinery cumbersome, expensive, and unreliable. Prices of electronic equipment rose, while performance fell.

Then it was found that the performance delivered by wires soldered into assemblies could be reproduced by conductors printed on sheet material. A circuit that did not require wires was developed.

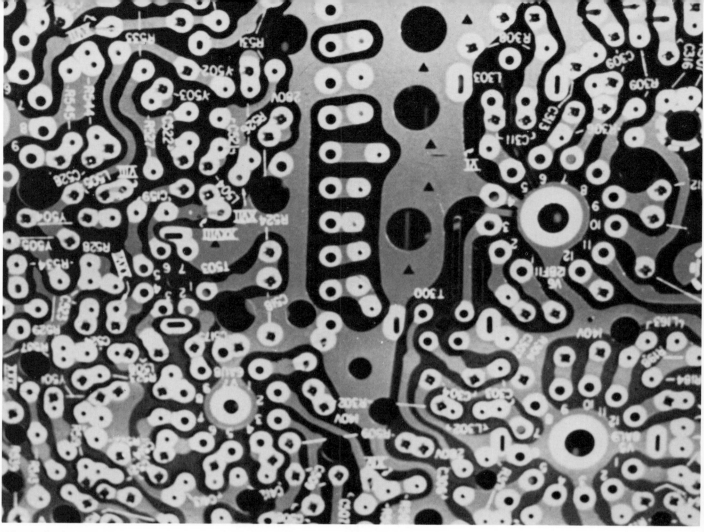

Printed circuit.

The printed circuit proved to have a number of advantages over conventional wired circuits. Aside from speed of assembly it integrated a series of elements which previously had been considered separately: the wire, resistors, connectors, and chassis. It prompted a "systems view" focusing on larger-scale components rather than elements. As a result of the widespread acceptance of the innovation, the price of these components has fallen enough to create an international market while cricuits of incredible complexity are now easily reproduced and miniaturized.

This new view of both process and product has revolutionized the production, servicing, and development of electronic equipment. Major improvements in the production of buildings will depend on a similar image shift.

The idea of putting a rocket on an apartment house to ship it once seemed revolutionary. But today we have seen fifty-story high structures leave Cape Kennedy for the moon. Most of the recent innovations in buildings are like this, putting a jet engine on an old-fashioned house. (Sketch by Buckminster Fuller's draftsman and students 1927–28, from *The Dymaxion World of Buckminster Fuller,* Reinhold Publishing Company.)

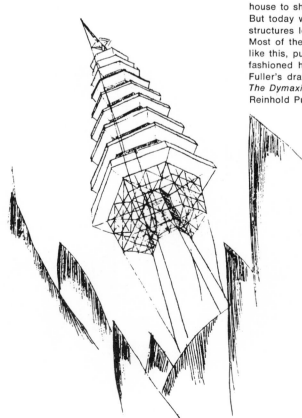

the filing cabinet

"Any idea in good currency is no longer appropriate to Its situation."
—Donald Schon

At first, Schon's statement may sound cynical, but it is, in fact, dealing with a very important question. Today, industrialized building has become an "idea in good currency." Let us now see how it developed and moved into the center of the stage.

The concept is not new. We can find references to it well before the beginning of this century. Le Corbusier was one of the first major architects to call for a move in this direction. He wrote in 1930:

> *"The task is to define and apply new and clear methods enabling the making of useful dwelling plans which lend themselves for execution in a natural way for standardization and industrialization."*

Corbusier stands out as an early champion of the new technology, but there were many others. In 1936 Albert Farwell Bemis wrote a powerful plea for order, rationality, and the new techniques in building in the three volumes of *The Evolving House*. No one involved in building could argue with his statement:

> *"For more years than I like to contemplate, it has seemed to me that the means of providing homes in modern America and elsewhere have been strangely out of date."*

Six years later, in the midst of World War II, the *Architectural Forum* ran a series called "Building's Postwar Pattern." In their call for change, they pointed out that:

> *". . . In no other field of economic and social endeavor is production so involved, assembly so disorganized, distribution so devious. In no other field is there so large a number of separately functioning organizations between raw material and ultimate consumer, such haphazard diversity of product, price, and performance."*

Business picked up the thread. In the late 1940's *Fortune Magazine* visited the site of an aircraft factory converted to manufacture Buckminster Fuller's Dymaxion House. "Wichita," they wrote, "will be the Kitty Hawk of housing."

Over and over again, from Alexander Graham Bell and Grovner Atterbury to the Bauhaus and Buckminster Fuller, we have been given the impression that the mass production of houses was the answer to the problem of improved housing. With this background it was not surprising to hear George Romney, Secretary of the U. S. Department of Housing and Urban Development, say (in the spring of 1969):

> *"We are now just in the first stage of the industrial age in housing production. . . . Before the seventies are over, industrialized housing will dominate the market."*

With a passion indicating the growing force of the idea, he went on:

> *"I believe the decade ahead is going to see a revolution in housing construction unmatched since men came out the caves and started building dwellings with their hands."*

DUCKER'S PORTABLE BARRACK AND FIELD HOSPITAL.

The Society of the Red Cross in Europe has, for several years, given particular attention to the subject of portable field hospitals and other improved appliances for the care of sick and wounded soldiers. Though

the mor
ferences
creasing
there is
those wh

When the Secretary of HUD is behind an idea, it is obviously in good currency, but a more powerful argument exists. Secretary Romney's speech was made almost a year after the following statement appeared in a letter to the *Playboy Forum:*

"As long as houses are individually produced by the medieval craft industry methods still used in most construction, decent housing will only come about over a period of generations, as the Government can be induced to subsidize it. But modern mass-production methods and portable-by-air-delivery concepts in housing solve the problem of 'doing more with less.'"

[$3.20 per Annum.
[POSTAGE PREPAID.]

method of settling international dif-
tion is appealing each year with in-
ss to the conscience of Christendom,
mense field for the ministrations of
conservation of life in the midst of its

military destroyers. Despite the deadliness of modern
instruments of warfare, it is conceded that a greater proportion of soldiers die from lack of sufficient care and
from exposure than from the immediate effects of the

(Continued on page 404.)

Sci. Am. N.Y.

Photo courtesy of National Forest Products Association.

Photo courtesy of Sikorsky Aircraft.

Industrialized building is obviously an idea in good currency.

Today almost everyone believes that industrialized housing will solve the problem. But if influential people have believed it for some time, if it has been government policy for years, if leading architects have believed it, and major manufacturers have believed it—it is fair to ask, "Why is it not working?" Why does the housing situation get worse each year as builders continue to talk about industrialization? Why is it that most other areas of manufacture have been industrialized to the point where the problem has become one of over-production rather than underproduction? Is this "idea in good currency" of the industrialization of building one which is inappropriate to our situation? Why is it that, up to now, industrialization has done so little to solve problems in building.

Perhaps it is because we are talking about change where there is no framework within which change can occur. We talk about new concepts, but we have no conceptual framework in which to organize the changes that are taking place. In the jargon of the "systems" people, what we are talking about is "information overload."

There is an analogy which may clarify this idea of conceptual framework, and how it relates with information overload.

The analogy I have in mind is a filing system.*

*Gary Stonebreaker suggests this analogy in his paper "The Impact of Social and Technical Change on Building." See the bibliography for a detailed reference.

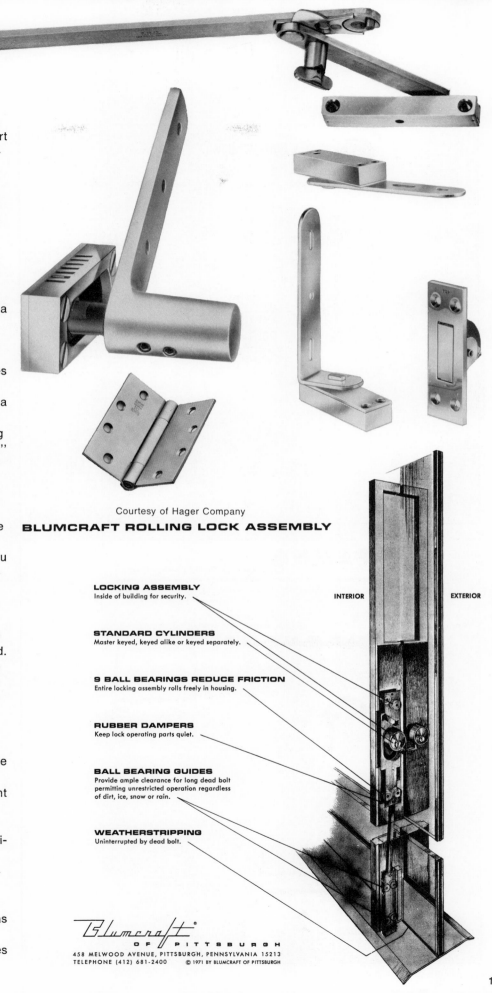

Let us look at it in familiar terms. To operate in any field one must start a filing system to deal with the problem of storing and finding important bits of information. In architecture, one begins to organize the system while still a student. While working on a problem, the student starts to collect information. Perhaps he is designing a playground. He collects magazine articles on playgrounds, photographs of playgrounds, notes, data, papers, etc. He sets up a manila folder and labels it: "Playgrounds." Soon there is another folder labeled "Houses." It contains house plans, data, and even details of some houses he likes. Perhaps he has done some work on hospitals; then there will be a folder for "Hospitals." Certainly by the time he finishes school, the young architect will have an "Office Building" file, a "School" file, and a "Housing" file. It is an easy system to use. When in need of information about playgrounds or housing, he looks through the drawer and picks out the appropriate folder. When you have information that you want to store, you simply put it into a folder. Occasionally a problem comes up—does a school playground go into "School" or "Playgrounds"? But the file is small, and a quick search will locate it no matter where it has been placed.

Let us look ahead a little, and see the file a few years later. Our young architect, having started to practice, has his first commission to design a small house. Suddenly the housing file is not very helpful. Now he needs more than some good house plans and examples of well-drawn elevations. One needs quite a different kind of information in order to write effective specifications to draw and dimension clear plans and to anticipate contractors' bids. The young architect needs information on doorknobs, bathtubs, windows, door frames, floor finishes, and a host of other building components. He begins to collect this information in his "House" file. Soon he sets up subfiles

Courtesy of Hager Company

BLUMCRAFT ROLLING LOCK ASSEMBLY

LOCKING ASSEMBLY
Inside of building for security.

INTERIOR   EXTERIOR

STANDARD CYLINDERS
Master keyed, keyed alike or keyed separately.

9 BALL BEARINGS REDUCE FRICTION
Entire locking assembly rolls freely in housing.

RUBBER DAMPERS
Keep lock operating parts quiet.

BALL BEARING GUIDES
Provide ample clearance for long dead bolt permitting unrestricted operation regardless of dirt, ice, snow or rain.

WEATHERSTRIPPING
Uninterrupted by dead bolt.

Blumcraft
OF PITTSBURGH
458 MELWOOD AVENUE, PITTSBURGH, PENNSYLVANIA 15213
TELEPHONE (412) 681-2400   © 1971 BY BLUMCRAFT OF PITTSBURGH

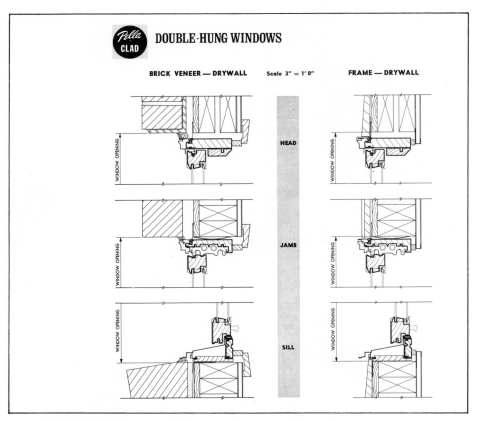

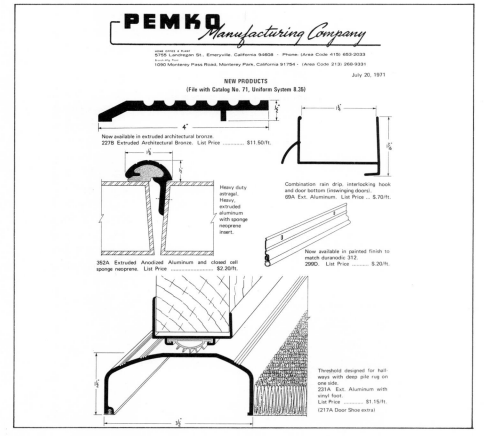

—"Doorknob" files, "Bathtub" files, "Window," "Door," and many other files. Each is filled with catalogues. As more and more information piles up, it becomes difficult to find. As other commissions come into the office, he may often be required to sort through the entire file cabinet before it occurs to him that one tile is in with bathrooms, while another was put with wall or floor finishes. He finds he is duplicating information; the same tile catalogue is in his "School" file as well as his "House" file. The system is now bulky and clumsy.

The intelligent architect finds that it is not such a difficult problem to solve. Other architects have had the same problem and an information system has been designed to handle it. In answer to this need, the American Institute of Architects has developed a way to file this body of information. One can buy an outline which describes the system: coordinating product categories with those commonly used by the distributors of manufacturer's literature. Bathtubs will be found in Section 10.7, wood windows in 8.16, and aluminum windows in 8.15. It is an easy matter to set up file cabinets in this way. Now, every time the architect receives new material, he consults his index card and then files bathtubs in 10.7 and wood windows in 8.16. When he wants to find something he again consults the master list to find it. He has a conceptual framework that fits his information.

UPGRADING PROPERTY?

RESiFORM
BATHROOM UNITS

Then an interesting problem arises. One day the mail brings our architect a catalogue from a manufacturer who makes entire bathrooms. The bathroom is built as one piece; it has a bathtub, a toilet, a sink, even a medicine cabinet, towel bars, and floor tile. Where does one put this information? Our architect thinks for a while and, as he is a creative soul—after all, that is why he is an architect—he comes up with a good solution.

He makes several Xerox copies. He puts one in the bathroom file, one in the medicine cabinet file, etc. After that, whenever he needs a bathtub, he will come across the package bathroom. This works well for a while, but the problem is not solved. The next week he receives a wall panel catalogue, and the wall panel has windows, doors, insulation, and electrical equipment in it. It requires another 10 Xerox copies. His Xerox bill is mounting, and at the same time, he notices that the cabinet is getting full. The cost of dealing with the new information is too high.

So our architect takes another clever, but predictable step. He sets up a "Miscellaneous File!"

He takes the package bathroom and the wall panel and all the products which do not fit the standard categories, and puts them in a miscellaneous file. From then on, whenever he has something that does not fit his framework, he will go to the miscellaneous file. It works pretty well, and it saves Xerox costs and cabinet space. Since they do not fit any other categories, we know that package bathrooms, wall panels, and prefab closets are all in the miscellaneous file.

This is a reasonable way to deal with information up to a point. But that point has been reached in many architects' offices. Standing at the cabinet one day, we realize that the miscellaneous file is bigger than the rest of the categories. It is so large that we can no longer find things in it.

That is what we mean by information overload. The point has been reached where the ideas we have for structuring information, the ways we have of looking at the world, and making things fit do not match the kind of information we have. When that happens, almost everything is put into a miscellaneous file.

Building is at that point today.

The conceptual framework we have is the house. What do we see when we picture a house? Perhaps a white clapboard frame, redwood shingles, or a crisp white modern box with a flat roof. But "house" itself is a relatively limited concept, considering all the things in our miscellaneous file. Air conditioning equipment, cable television, two cars, and trash mashers represent new hardware, just as play-rooms, TV rooms, and family rooms represent new life styles. We have a real problem of information overload. Our miscellaneous file is so big we cannot deal with all the bits of information available to us.

We do the best we can. Whenever we come across new information, whenever we find a new tool, whenever we hear of a new technique or discover a new material, we try to fit it into the old framework. As McLuhan says, "We are riding into the future with our eyes on the rearview mirror."

We are trying to put a jet engine on a horse to modernize the pony express.

With this analogy in mind, let us go on to examine some of the new elements which have been placed in our miscellaneous file and see if we can use this understanding to anticipate the shift that will take us to a new conceptual framework for building. Let us see if there is not another way to look at the new technologies—a form of industrialized building which is more than factories making houses.

TYPICAL SPECIFICATION

Excavator

Excavate oversite to reduce levels and to form downstand around perimeter of slab as required.

Concrete Foundations

Lay on 2" concrete blinding, 4" thick lightly reinforced concrete slab, including thickening to underside of slab to form toe, slab finished smooth to receive Resiform Unit.

Lay polythene sheet on 4" smooth finished slab.

Make necessary drain connections to allow for connection to prefabricated unit drain outlet.

Prefabricated Units

Supply, fix to slab and connect to existing building prefabricated 'Resiform' bathroom unit, to be delivered to site completely finished and lifted into position by a suitable crane.

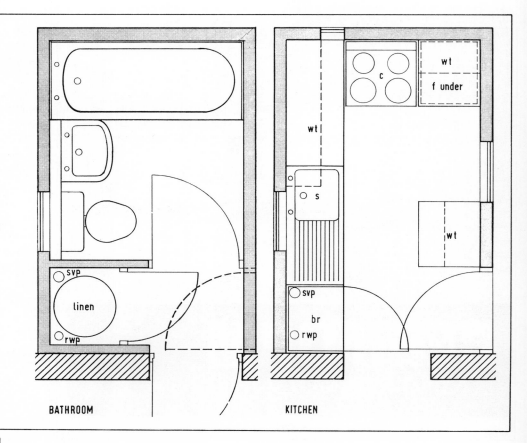

BATHROOM   KITCHEN

Courtesy William Old (Resiform) Limited

Above photos courtesy of Automated Building Components, Inc.

the contents of the miscellaneous file

Houses built today are influenced by recent changes in the materials and methods of construction. In most instances they are also built by a new kind of building organization, as part of a new manufacturing and marketing structure, and under a building program which has been recently introduced. In more and more instances, the house conforms to new standards and new research.

These changes have occurred as a result of the acceptance of methods and techniques of industrial manufacturing. Three parallel forces brought this about: (1) the development of large construction organizations to undertake building programs as a result of the Depression and World War II; (2) the adoption of new materials such as plastics, plywood, and high-strength steel, which were developed by industries more technologically advanced than the building industry; and (3) the rapid development, after World War II, of industrialized methods as the answer to shortages of housing, skilled labor, and materials.

Within the building industry itself we can trace two sets of interconnected developments. The first includes changes in *materials and methods:*

1. The introduction of new processes between the source of raw materials and the building.

2. The introduction of new building materials, tools, and products.

3. The transfer of part of the building process from the site to the factory.

4. The introduction of industrially produced components, buildings, and building systems.

5. The use of industrial methods to produce products, components, assemblies, and finished units of increasingly larger size.

The second group of changes involves the *structure of the industry:*

1. Building as an assembly operation. We have seen that the introduction of mass production techniques and prefabricated components has begun to take the craft out of building technology and to replace the small-time contractor with the entrepreneur of the building industry.

2. The role of the manufacturer has changed as his product has become more specifically related to a building.

3. New markets have been developed as traditional ones change to include new products and services for new customers in a new context.

4. A clear framework of standards becomes increasingly important as buildings, building materials, and building institutions change.

5. The need for research is becoming critical as the basis for standards, goals, and the development of new products.

Photo courtesy of Automated Building Systems, Inc.

TYPE OF HOUSE	OFF-SITE WORK	ON-SITE WORK
LOG CABIN 		- FELL TREES - SHAPE AND FIT LOGS - HEW PLANKS FOR ROOF, FLOOR, FURNITURE, ETC.
EARLY BALLOON FRAME 	- MILL LUMBER - PRODUCE HARDWARE AND PAINT - FACTORY-MAKE FURNITURE	- CUT AND FIT LUMBER FOR FRAMING, SIDING, ETC. - CONSTRUCT WINDOWS, DOORS, STAIRS, CABINETS - PLASTER - PAINT AND FINISH
CONVENTIONAL FRAME 	- MILL LUMBER - PRODUCE HARDWARE AND PAINT - FACTORY-MAKE FURNITURE, CABINETRY, WINDOWS, DOORS, STAIRS, WALLBOARD	- CUT AND FIT LUMBER FOR STRUCTURE AND CLOSURE - INSTALL FACTORY-MADE COMPONENTS - PAINT AND FINISH
PACKAGE HOME 	- DESIGN AND FABRICATE A SET OF COORDINATED BUILDING COMPONENTS FOR STRUCTURE/CLOSURE, PLUMBING CORES, WINDOWS, DOORS, INTERIOR DIVIDERS AND STORAGE UNITS	- ASSEMBLE PREFABRICATED COMPONENTS
MOBILE OR SECTIONAL HOME 	- FABRICATE COMPLETE FACTORY-MADE HOUSE WITH ALL FINISHES AND APPOINTMENTS	

Plastic structure by architect R. J. Thom of Toronto, Ontario. (Photo courtesy of Expo Corporation.)

1. The introduction of new processes between the source of raw material and the building

The building industry's first steps toward industrialization were taken when processes were introduced between the source of materials and the building. These innovations involved some of the most traditional materials.

MASONRY   The industrialization of building began as far back as Babylon, with the invention of brick, the most ancient of prefabricated elements. When made from local materials to the craftsman's dimensions, at the site, brick was free of the problems of dimensional standards, damage during shipping, and adaptability to local conditions. But, recently, the large investment required for the machinery to mass-produce masonry units has made the centralization of production economically necessary. Now the weight of the units and their brittle nature affect handling, shipping, and the distribution system. The difficulty of cutting brick at the site, for example, has made dimensional standards essential. These standards which are adapted to the materials, production, shipping, and handling process at one end begin to limit the possibilities of the designer at the other.

LUMBER   With the introduction of the sawmill to replace hand hewn logs at the building site a revolution began in wood construction. From the moment that a tree is cut into boards, the design alternatives are limited. Each decision made, from the development of standards by which lumber is graded, treated, and shaped, to the storage and distribution systems by which it reaches the building, has an enormous affect on building design. The transition from the log cabin to the balloon frame is an excellent illustration of the nature of this change.

2. The introduction of new building materials, tools, and products

New materials have been introduced into the building industry from a number of areas. The main influx of change has come from more advanced technologies. Innovations from the chemical and metals industries (plastics, aluminum, and high-strength steel) have been significant, as have tools methods and materials borrowed from the automobile and aircraft industries. However, the introduction of new materials has been slowed by the conservatism of the building field. Those materials which improve performance at lower cost without radically changing appearance such as aluminum siding, plastic coatings on wood, and painted metal doors have been more successful than those which conflict with traditional procedures of production, marketing, and obtaining official acceptance.

Among the most significant recent developments have been innovations in plastics, metals, concrete, sheet materials, and tools.

PLASTICS   The introduction of plastics into the building industry is an excellent example of an input from the chemical industry and illustrates a way in which completely new materials and processes may be adapted to building.

Soon after the introduction of polyvinylchloride (PVC), in 1936, the manufacturers of plastics began to see the building industry as an enormous potential market. With a family of over a dozen plastic materials in production and in use in other industries, the plastic manufacturers turned to building at the end of World War II.

(Above and below) The Monsanto House of architects Goody and Clancy.

Many of their early experiments, such as the "Monsanto House of the Future," sought to use reinforced plastics to revolutionize the structure of housing. This house used plastics as plastics rather than in the form of traditional materials. In it the enormous number of framing parts used in traditional buildings was reduced to a few large sandwich panels combining most of the building elements. But the Monsanto House did not capture a significant part of the market. Production was out of the main-stream of the building industry. Its construction conformed to no building codes, and the investment necessary to vary the components was too high to allow for real flexibility. As a result it was eventually abandoned.

At this time, producers realized that they could find a significant market for plastic materials in housing without building the basic structure of plastic. This approach avoided most of the problems of code compliance, design, marketing, contracting, and financing which accompany responsibility for the structure of a building.

The Monsanto House by architects Goody and Clancy.

The Monsanto House by architects Goody and Clancy.

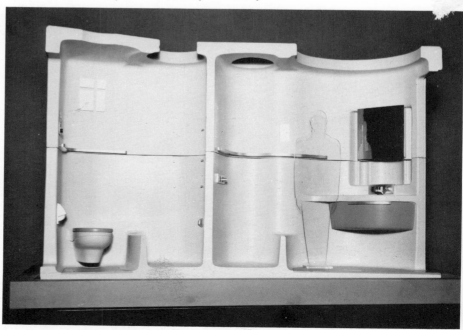

The Monsanto House by architects Goody and Clancy.

Unbreakable plastic windows. (Photo courtesy of General Telephone Company.)

Classic grandeur
in wood or fiberglass
...custom built
to specifications by

Somerset
DOOR & COLUMN CO.

"Classic grandeur in wood or fiberglass . . ."

For this reason we have seen the development of plastic substitutes for almost every one of the conventional materials in building construction. These range from protective plastic coatings affording decoration, durability, and ease of maintenance through light-transmitting materials for such items as skylights and light fixtures, to insulation, pipes, furniture, and fabrics. The growth of plastics continues to increase more rapidly than the growth rate of the building industry itself. There is hardly a traditional building product that does not have a plastic counterpart.

Plastic flooring in the form of vinyls, carpet, sheet materials, and coatings for wood and masonry is widely used. Plastic provides electric and acoustic insulation as well as thermal control. It is used for glazing in garages and greenhouses, for exterior panels, sunshades, sealants, pipe, gutters, downspouts, garage doors, and screens. Products like plastic sheet material, used as damp-proofing

Rigid urethane foam plastic beams by William Products, Inc.

under slabs and on wooden walls, have changed the work of masons and carpenters. Reinforced plastic bath fixtures and whole bathrooms of molded plastic are now commonly available.

Today we find plastic components edging their way into the structural components of building. Plastic forms for reinforced concrete are common, plastic panels are often load bearing, and special structures such as Dow's "Spiral Generation" domes of styrofoam, or Bird-Air's translucent plastic fabrics which are inflated by low-pressure air handling equipment are used to span large column-free spaces.

In most of their present applications plastics find no legal difficulties. There are, however, exceptions. Fire-resistance of structural members and the inherent problems of smoke and flame spread are questioned by the building code authorities as are the properties of corrosion, temperature dimensional variation, and vermin resistance. Plastics are marketed through traditional channels and assembled by traditional building organizations. Architects, builders, labor, financial institutions, and the user are convinced of their value. Thus, plastics seem destined to play an increasingly larger role in building.

(Above photos) Air structures by Birdair.

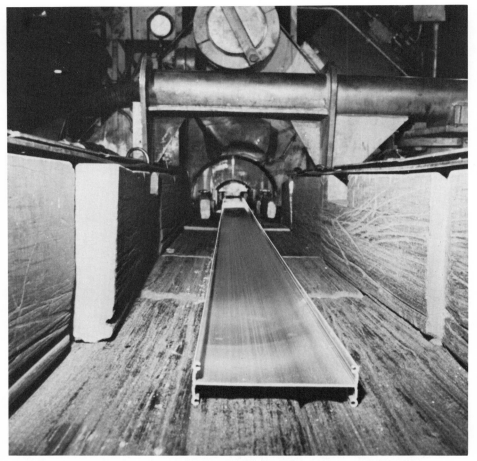

Extruded building frame member. (Photo courtesy of Aluminum Company of America.)

METALS Metal products entered the building industry in much the same way as plastics. The machine-made nail, developed in the first years of the nineteenth century, helped to launch the industrialization of building through the balloon frame. The rolled steel structural section, a spin-off of early railroad technology, made high-rise buildings possible. However, it was the development of a new metallurgy for World War II which launched the widespread use of new metal products in building.

Early attempts to produce a metal house from the "Lustron House" in the mid 1940's to the "Alside House" in 1964 all failed when unexpected problems of financing distribution, and the cost of production, added to inflexibility and unfamiliarity of design could not provide the margin of profit necessary to develop marketing structures. These houses could not overcome the popular prejudice as to what a house should be nor could they meet the objectives of local builders, labor, and building codes. But again, as in the case of plastics, metal products began to appear in many traditional forms.

Alcoa Alumiframe residential building system. (Photo courtesy of Aluminum Company of America.)

Alcoa residential building system is similar to a wood framing system. (Photo courtesy of Aluminum Company of America.)

Photo courtesy of Aluminum Company of America.

Aluminum, because of its light weight and corrosion-resistance, has been widely used for windows, roofing, siding, and sliding doors, as well as for flashing and trim. Thin sheets of aluminum are used in reflective insulation. It is also widely used as finished wall panels with color added by annodizing, porcelain, and plastic coatings. Today, we find aluminum as the most common of the exterior finishes used in the booming mobile home industry.

Steel has found widespread use in areas remote from its traditional structural role. Most of the material used in household equipment, such as dishwashers and laundry equipment, heating and air conditioning units, is made of steel. It is also used in furniture, hardware, and a variety of wall panels.

With the introduction of high-strength steels and new national standards, steel has been brought into sharper competition with concrete in high-rise and long-span structures. Recent improvements in bolting and welding have made erection easier. New techniques of fabrication increase the competitive position of steel products. For example, since flat stock can now be economically welded into a variety of shapes, the fabricator can remain flexible without a large inventory of special shapes.

Recent years have brought new attempts to develop steel housing systems by diverse groups. Steel systems for package warehouse and commercial buildings are common and several of the School Construction Systems Development (SCSD) competitors have marketed school building systems which use steel roof deck, structural members, ceiling systems, and steel partition systems. The "Staggered Truss System," developed at M.I.T. under a grant from the U.S. Steel Co., offers ease of erection, long spans, plan flexibility, and wind resistance for tall buildings. The key to the widespread use of prestressed concrete is the high-strength steel used in tendons.

As with plastics, most of these innovations entered the building field in the form of traditional products using traditional marketing and distribution systems to fit traditional design themes and to meet the requirements of existing financing and codes.

Before the full potential of steel in building can be realized there must be changes in codes and standards making it possible to take full advantage of steel's qualities. We must be able to employ "plastic design" more fully and more rational fire protection requirements must be established. New markets must be created similar to those aggregated by SCSD and the mobile home industry if we are to provide enough volume to encourage research. In such a situation the development of new products and the economic use of materials such as high-strength and heat-resistance steels or aluminum alloys developed by more advanced technologies could be introduced to housing.

Photo courtesy of Aluminum Company of America.

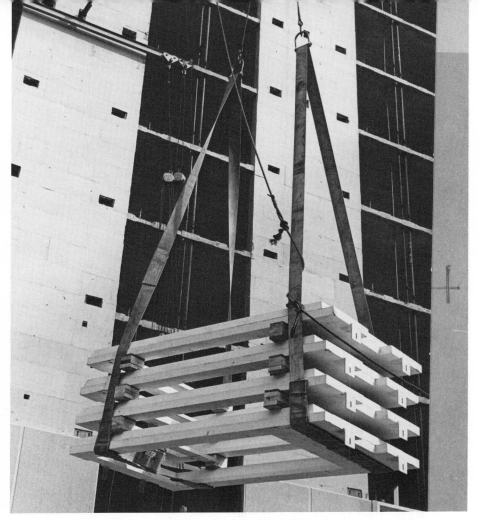

Precast concrete panels, New York City. (Photo by Forrest Wilson.)
Russian precast housing system, Moscow. (Photo by Forrest Wilson.)

CONCRETE   This traditional material has advanced technically while maintaining its general appearance, market and production characteristics. Availability, economy, fire-proof, and insulation characteristics combined with the development of improved reinforcing through welded mesh and deformed bars as well as new tools and techniques for forming and placing bars have made concrete popular for buildings of all sorts.

With the general acceptance of precasting and prestressing techniques, more widespread and imaginative uses of concrete are appearing. But this area of development will not be fully explored until a number of nontechnical problems are solved. Industry-wide standards for dimension, connection, and materials must be evolved and accepted locally. Methods of inspecting and certifying work transported across local and state boundaries must be developed. New equipment for fabricating, transporting, and placing precast components must be found and a new labor category, the concrete erector, must be recognized.

SHEET MATERIALS   Many sheet materials have recently been introduced in building. Plywood is probably the most well known, but plasterboard, fiber and hardboards, wood chipboards, cement-asbestos boards, plastic laminates, and sheet vinyls are all being used to speed erection. They also reduce the number of pieces in an assembly and reduce on-site labor. The rapid acceptance of these products can be expected since they increase strength, rigidity, and weathertightness. They can be shaped and fitted at the site by traditional crafts and do not require manufacture to close tolerences. They can also be given a wide variety of finishes and surface treatments.

While prefinishing of surface materials helps to reduce the amount of site work, it often necessitates higher dimensional tolerance and special joint systems. Without a well-designed joint, prefinished materials require expensive hand finishing such as the taping, spackling, and painting of plasterboard or the extruded aluminum mouldings for plywood panels. Code acceptance is not usually a problem with sheet materials. They can be mass-produced in a few factories and nationally distributed from these sources. Shipping is also not a problem, although truck size and maneuverability limit the dimension of flat sheets. With few exceptions, such as plasterers vs. plasterboard, labor and traditional craft subcontractors have rapidly adapted these new materials.

The significant thread running through these innovations is their widespread acceptance and use. Building materials lose their local and regional characteristics and become national involving large investments on the part of the manufacturers and wide markets to support these investments. They depend on a framework of national standards, national distribution systems, widespread and organized demand, and local interest in contracting the work. Without this framework the most promising of new material will not be absorbed into the building process.

Panelized building method by O'Connor Lumber Company.
TRW housing system using sheet material.

(Top, left) Photo courtesy of Aluminum Company of America.

(Top, right) Photo courtesy of Automated Building Components.

Use of air compressor and hose to supply air for stapling of asphalt shingles. (Photo courtesy of SENCO Products, Inc.)

TOOLS It is difficult to imagine carpenters framing a house today without the hand-held power saw. Yet a generation ago its use was unknown. Power hand tools, drills, sanders, and routers have reduced the skill and human energy needed for on-site carpentry while increasing the output and the capital investment required by builders.

The introduction of these tools shortly after World War II was a crucial factor in meeting the Postwar housing demand without significantly increasing the number of skilled craftsmen. Their use grew in parallel to the new family of sheet materials introduced in building. With the hand-held power saw the long cuts required to rip 8-foot long plywood sheets, masonite, and insulation board could be made quickly, easily, and accurately by relatively unskilled workmen.

New tools have lessened the skill and speeded the operation of hanging doors and setting door hardware, changed the techniques of fastening wood flooring, and speeded the drilling required to open wood structures to receive the increasing quantities of pipes and wiring needed to accommodate appliances.

Lifting, moving, and carrying tools have taken most of the heavy labor out of loading and unloading materials, raising large pieces such as trusses and laminated wooden beams, grading, digging, and the host of operations common to building.

Proof of this development lies in the fact that one of the first concerns of the builder today has become the supply of power to the site. If the service is not available, he must bring in portable generators; if a fuse blows, most operations cease.

Automated nailer toe-nailing studs. (Photo courtesy of SENCO Products, Inc.)

Applying cedar shingles with automatic stapler. (Photo courtesy of SENCO Products, Inc.)

Service van with equipment for service and repair of automatic building tools. (Photo courtesy of SENCO Products, Inc.)

In another area, the introduction of portable welding and inspection equipment has made the use of site-welded connections possible in steel frames. The clumsy, slow, and man-power-consuming riveting operation of former times has given way to a simpler process which also provides increased rigidity through joint continuity. An entire family of portable welding tools has become familiar on construction jobs. It is now possible to use steel with increased flexibility and to make continuous connections in the reinforcing of precast concrete building elements.

Recently a number of sophisticated machine tools have entered the building factory. High levels of automation are now familiar in the production of building materials such as steel, brick, and concrete and in the manufacture of building components. This has also happened with the production of hardware, window and door assemblies, millwork, and plumbing fixtures. Numerically controlled automated tools have even been applied to the production of wood frame construction. Today several companies manufacture automated nailing machines. Machine tool transfer systems are finding increasing use in the machining and assembly of stud wall units, finished walls, and components. Mobile and sectional home manufacturers place a high value on this reduction in the skilled labor required for production, the uniformity of quality, and the variety of operations which effectively reduce capital costs.

Factory manufacture of wall panels. (Photo courtesy of SENCO Products, Inc.)

(Top, right) Photo courtesy of Hydro-Air Engineering, Inc.

(Bottom right) Nailing machine on ceiling assembly line. (Photo courtesy of Levitt Building Systems.)

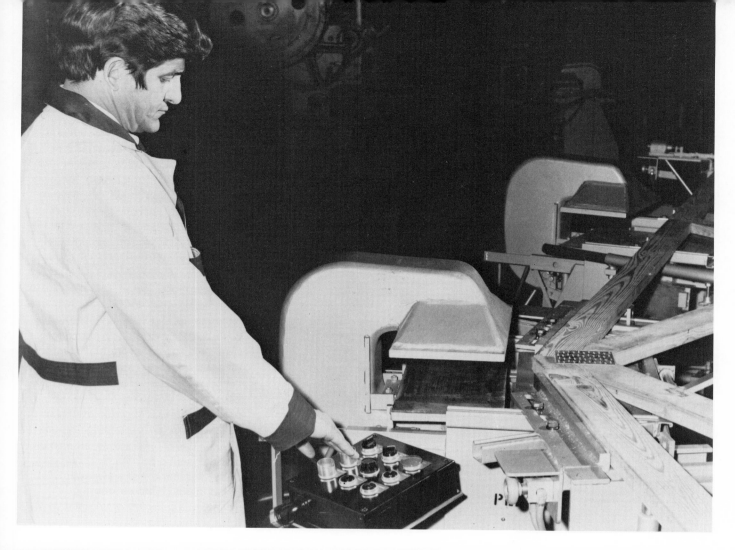

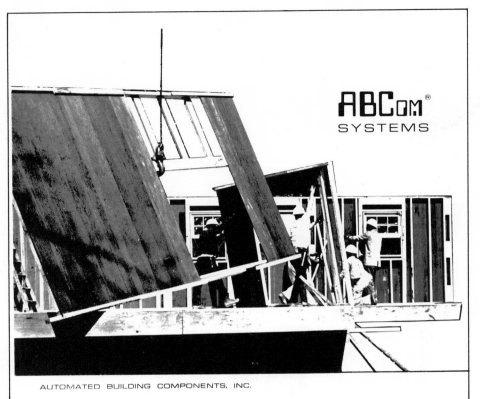

ABCom®
SYSTEMS

AUTOMATED BUILDING COMPONENTS, INC.

With the introduction of smaller and cheaper mini-computers and satellite sequencing controllers into numerically controlled transfer systems, we can anticipate a more versatile approach to production. Building subassemblies and assemblies are now controlled efficiently. Although many of the new factories use these tools to speed production of conventional wood shingle houses, it is the product and not the process which is an anachronism. The tools promise uniform quality in broad diversity. They afford a high degree of parts interchangeability, adherence to strict dimensional tolerances which hold over long production runs, and a reduction of the fatigue of operators. By permitting the use of unskilled workers they promote low labor costs.

We can expect the availability of these tools to make enormous changes in building once used in an appropriate framework.

ABCom® SYSTEMS.....total computerized building

Automated Building Components, Inc., the country's leader in construction prefabrication methods, has just introduced the ABCom System to the building industry. ABCom Systems are a group of computer programs that give the builder, prefabricator, supplier, architect and others immediate low cost solutions to today's construction problems.

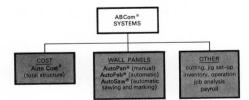

AutoPan® SYSTEM.....first of the ABCom® Systems

The first of the ABCom Systems introduced is AutoPan. It is a computer supported technique for quickly converting any custom or standard floor plan drawing of a frame building into detailed fabrication instructions for all interior and exterior wall components of that building. AutoPan also provides a complete bill of materials for the walls arranged for simple costing, a cutting bill, a computer drawn diagram of the floor plan for verification and wall erection instructions.

This system was in development for several years at Imperial Components, Inc., Charlottesville, Virginia. It has been used daily in their wall panel production for over a year.

How the system functions

The AutoPan System is available through timesharing computer centers throughout the United States. The user does not have an investment in costly computers, but only a teletype terminal located in his office so the computer center may be contacted immediately. Technical training on computers is not required, as a simple three-day class instructs office personnel on the preparation of computer input data. Any typist can transmit the required code information to the processing center.

The costs involved are (1) actual computer and plotter time charges incurred and (2) a charge per lineal foot of wall processed by AutoPan. Savings are reflected in time saved, elimination of costly errors and rapid expansion of panel output with the same staff.

Who can use AutoPan?

Due to the complete flexibility of AutoPan, anyone framing walls or wall panels may profit by its services. The method enables large fabricators to free key personnel for other jobs and establish production capacity at any level with a small office staff. Smaller producers obtain accuracy of panel construction with instant costing details and cutting bills and only pay for the actual time the computer is in operation. AutoPan custom output is compatible to any manual or automated nailing method or equipment. The simplicity of AutoPan enables anyone to get into panel fabrication with a minimum investment in fabricating equipment and to expand production facilities at any rate desired. Pre fab house manufacturers, including mobile, modular and sectional houses can instantly modify standard designs by using AutoPan; they will have complete wall panel fabrication instructions, a bill of materials, cutting bill and a dimensioned floor plan.

Eliminates paper bottleneck

A highly skilled staff is no longer required to interpret the floor plan into shop and fabrication instructions. This normally lengthy function is now reduced to less than one hour, thus freeing highly paid personnel for other functions. A floor plan or general schematic is the basis for rapid coding of data for the computer. AutoPan eliminates the need for a take-off, item by item, as the code number assigned to a particular component (e. g. a door) instructs the computer to use certain information in making calculations for any one component. This information is already contained in the memory of the computer, and only this code number is required for its complete release. It is only necessary to divide the walls into convenient panel lengths indicating their appropriate physical details on the coding sheets. Costly mistakes are eliminated as the large number of variables are handled by the computer and errors are discovered before the wall panels are fabricated, not after.

(Near right) An "Exo-Skeleton": this device, already on the market, when energized allows a man to lift as much as 1000 pounds. The potential for this kind of development in parallel with larger building components promises major changes for the building constructor. (Drawn by David Brindle.)

(Far right) A Robot Building Constructor—typical of the aids to building erection we can expect to see at work on future projects. (Source: *The Future of the Future*, John McHale, George Braziller, Inc., New York, 1969.)

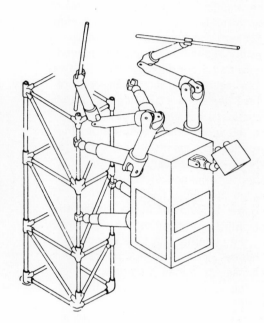

Using the terminal in your office

When the code sheet is completed, a typist will then transmit the coded information to the computer by teletype. At this point, the computer will evaluate the coded material, noting any errors in input. Using the geometry provided, the computer is actually building an intangible model of the house. From this model the computer can easily detect errors, such as improperly located windows, incorrect allowances for trim around a door frame, or wrong panel measuements. This information, known as error diagnostics, is transmitted back to the user's office on his teletype immediately. Corrections are made and transmitted back to the computer. As soon as there are no errors, the user requests the output from the computer.

All information received will be complete and accurate to 1/16th inch. The system verifies new model designs for accuracy before having miscalculations show up on the job.

Program data bank

During more than a year of constant use of the program a multitude of specifications and data have been stored in the memory of the computer. A special storage file is used for particular information which may be individual to only one user. This information may include special building code requirements or methods which may apply only to his wall panels.

What you get from AutoPan

Computer output consists of a complete accurate bill of material arranged for rapid costing, a cutting bill, detailed fabrication instructions and a plotter drawing of the floor plan indicating location and position of the panels.

Simple fabrication

Each page of the fabrication instructions print-out contains all the information necessary for the fabrication of a particular panel. Whether you are using a simple manual work table or sophisticated panel-building equipment, these instructions are all that are needed to build custom panels now. The plotter drawing will aid job-site tradesmen in the correct positioning of the finished panels in the structure.

Accuracy

All chance of human error in calculation is eliminated through the use of AutoPan in detailing wall panels. This accurate information is ready in a fraction of the time previously used in readying shop instructions. Finally, last-minute plan changes or

modifications requested by an architect or homeowner can be rapidly recalculated and compensated for in just a few seconds of the computer's time.

AutoSaw

With no additional coding a punched paper tape may be produced and teletyped to customer for use in an automated saw and marking machine. This machine cuts and marks lumber in the order required for fabrication, eliminating inventory of cut lumber.

Future programs

Now in development is AutoFab, a tape controlled line of equipment to completely assemble and nail wall panels. The machine uses bulk 16d nails and can assemble panels in either low or high volume production.

ABCom Systems will introduce AutoCost, a program that will plan and price-out the entire construction process of a building from foundation to roof.

AutoPan® Advantages

- Eliminates paperwork problem at low cost
- No item-by-item take-off of materials. Code does this
- Code complete structure in less than one hour
- Immediate return of complete bill of materials
- Accurate costs, not an estimate
- Cutting bill piece by piece
- Computer drawing of floor plan for erection
- Changes in house plan made easy
- Compatible with any production method in use
- Makes exact calculations by means of computer processing
- Step up estimating, production and delivery of jobs as required
- Fabrication instructions, printed or in punched tape form, to drive AutoSaw and AutoFab

Transfer of Part of the Building Process from Site to Factory

The transfer of part of the building process from site to factory began with the manufacture of brick and the milling of lumber. The increasing use of materials like steel, aluminum, precast concrete, plastics, and the variety of sheet materials had moved more and more design decisions away from the building site. With many of these decisions a building's characteristics are fixed and design decisions are made long before the architect is commissioned. Limitations are put on the design, construction, and performance of future buildings at the moment a tree is cut into boards. Buildings and the character of entire communities are determined by the acceptance of the standard shapes, sizes, and the composition of mass-produced materials.

The very use of certain of these materials limits the possibility of forming and finishing at the site. It is obviously impossible to roll steel beams, extrude aluminum sections, or manufacture composition board at each building site. It is evident that many jobs can be done more quickly, easily, and with greater economy, control, and precision at a work place where special skills, tools, and controls are available.

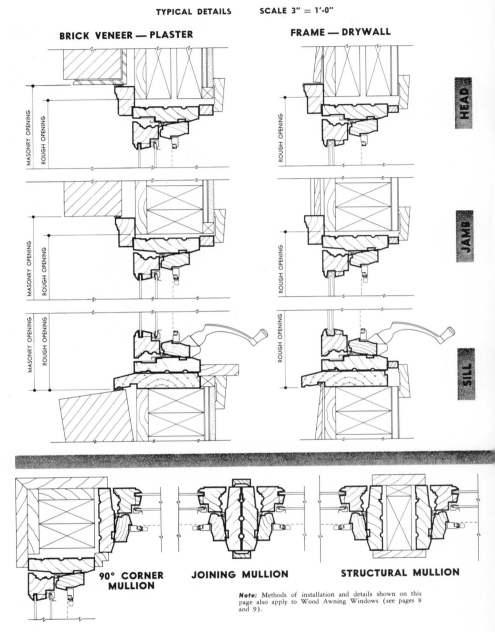

TYPICAL DETAILS   SCALE 3" = 1'-0"

BRICK VENEER — PLASTER   FRAME — DRYWALL

HEAD

JAMB

SILL

90° CORNER MULLION   JOINING MULLION   STRUCTURAL MULLION

Note: Methods of installation and details shown on this page also apply to Wood Awning Windows (see pages 8 and 9).

Courtesy of Rolscreen Company, Pella, Iowa.

MILLWORK   With the introduction
of power tools to shape lumber,
millwork was one of the first
operations to move from the site to the
factory. The on-site carpenter lost
much of his work to the millworker.
Power tools which were originally
set up at the site were first moved to
the builder's shop, then to the
lumber yard, and eventually to the
manufacturer as tools became more
complex, bulky, expensive, and
difficult to use. With the introduction
of manufactured woodwork, generally
acceptable standards evolved and
a distribution system developed.
Today it is a most unusual building
design which does not take advantage
of standard wood moulding, bases,
stair treads, handrails, saddles, door
and window trim.

(Right) Traditional factory tools. (Photo
courtesy of ALODEX Corp., Memphis, Tenn.)

(Bottom) The machine in the foreground nails,
sheaths, staples, routes, and trims woodwork.
(Photo courtesy of Clary Corporation.)

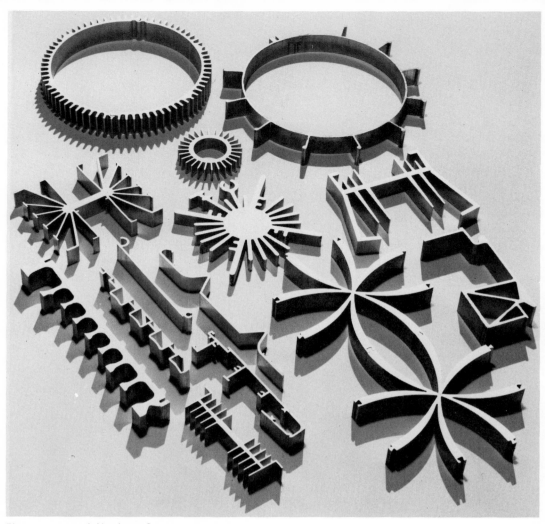

Photo courtesy of Aluminum Company of America.

extruded aluminum saddles

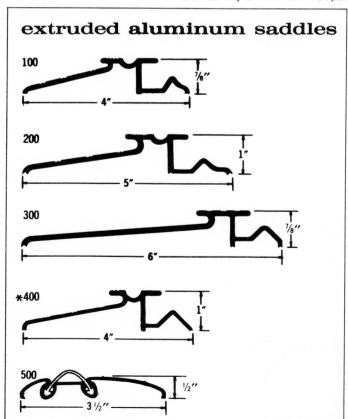

100   4"   7/8"

200   5"   1"

300   6"   7/8"

*400   4"   1"

500   3 1/2"   1/2"

A. NITT & SON

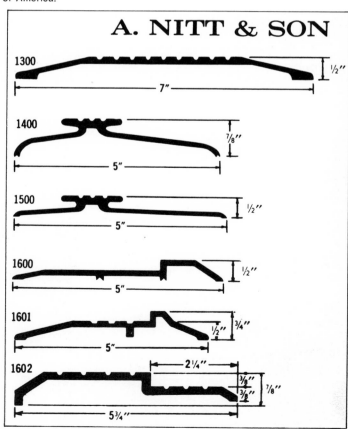

1300   7"   1/2"

1400   5"   7/8"

1500   5"   1/2"

1600   5"   1/2"

1601   5"   1/2"   3/4"

1602   5 3/4"   2 1/4"   3/8"   3/8"   7/8"

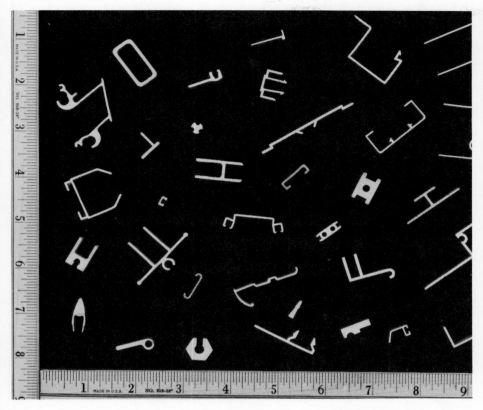

Although high tolerances are easily achieved in the profiles of these products, they are unnecessary in the length dimension since the carpenter cuts and fits the part with traditional tools and skill. His job increasingly becomes one of installation rather than joinery.

The development of aluminum and plastic extrusions eliminated many of the traditional functions of millwork. An aluminum sliding-door track and frame arrives at the job site completely formed and finished. It is a material of superior dimensional stability and low maintenance requirements. If it has been designed to fit the adjacent construction of the building it is easily installed. Gravel stops, gutters, downspouts, siding, and railings which were formerly only to be obtained in wood have now become common in metal and plastic. These materials can be and often are worked by common woodworking tools.

They are supplied by familiar distribution systems and present no conflict with local codes. As efficiency of production and distribution is added to ease of installation and maintenance, they tend to take over more and more of this woodwork market. However, unless standards are intelligently set and designs well made, they can undermine quality and limit the possibilities offered to the building's designer. Each new material or process takes the form of an earlier one. Rarely does the new material approach the problem on a scale broad enough to make full use of its inherent possibilities.

Photos courtesy of Aluminum Company of America.

METAL FABRICATING   Cutting, drilling, and assembly of a large percentage of most steel structures have taken place off the job site for sometime. The metal fabricating plants machine the work with great precision to exacting engineering specifications. Heavy lifting and shaping equipment and skilled workmen prepare the work for shipping and immediate erection at the site. The addition of other steel products such as sheet and corrugated decking, bar joists, and built up trusses to the steel frame results in "tailor made" structures, prepared by the manufacturer for assembly at the site.

Aluminum, plastics, and concrete can be treated in the same way. Standard or custom-made elements, factory-tailored to the designer's specifications, are packaged and shipped requiring only site assembly. This is often done by the fabricator's own crews.

With steel this procedure presents very few problems. The material is known, the construction visible and specialized assembly crews are common-place. But a similar use of precast concrete poses new problems such as the testing and certification of the material. Professional responsibility is more difficult to assign. The introduction of new skills in the work crews of concrete erectors to replace the traditional carpenters, lathers, and finishers must be developed. In many cases these problems have limited the extent of precasting to nonstructural applications such as curtain walls. We find that precast decorative panels fabricated in the concrete contractors' yards are often of much higher strength than the structural concrete poured in place at the job site.

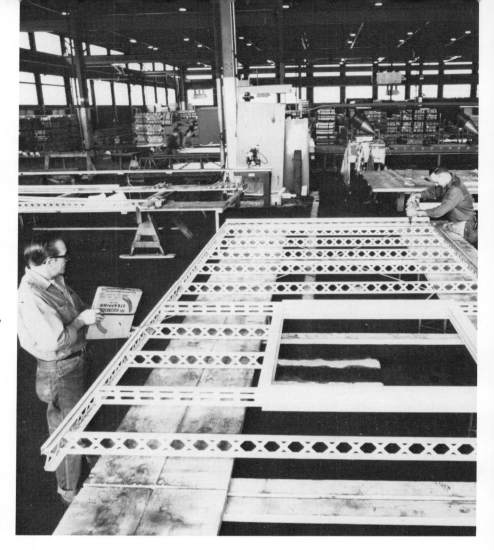

All photos courtesy of Aluminum Company of America.

44

PREFABRICATED TRUSSES   Among
the most successful off-site
fabricated elements have been
trusses. These can be made by carpenters in the builder's shop or local
lumberyard. They eliminate the
necessity for large production runs,
storage of inventory, and long
distance shipping and require no
special equipment. In addition truss
assemblies accelerate and simplify
the entire building process. Interior
footings, walls, and supports are
eliminated. This not only makes
planning more flexible, but also leaves
large areas open for finishing before
the partitions are erected. Houses
are closed-in faster with fewer
parts. These parts, though larger,
are easily handled with modifications
to equipment already on the job.
Construction crews can fabricate
trusses in slack periods or bad
weather and the trusses can be used
in traditional house design. All of
these factors have encouraged
builders to fight and overcome early
code restrictions to their use.

Photo courtesy of Hydro-Air Engineering, Inc.

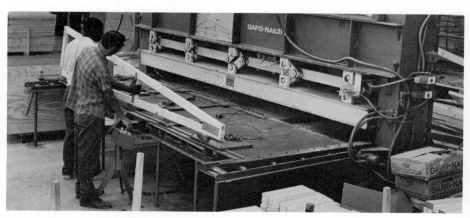

Above photos courtesy of Gang-Nail, Automated Building Components, Inc.

Above photos courtesy of Gang-Nail, Automated Building Components, Inc.

PREFINISHING   Anyone who has followed the day-by-day construction of a building will have noticed that progress is rapid as the frame rises and is enclosed. There then comes a time of disappointing slowdown from initial enclosure of the building to its completion. Many prefabricated structures, and even conventional wood frame housing shells can be enclosed in a few days; yet completion is months away. Finishing is one of the most time-consuming and expensive aspects of building. Fitting doors, laying floors, cabinet work, tile setting, cleaning, and painting not only take time but interfere with the workings of other trades. A late delivery, or a delay by any one craft, can stop or considerably slow the work. Whenever finished units can be brought to the site, there is the possibility of speeding construction.

For many of these installations, such as door, window, or cabinet units, code and labor problems are not restrictive. Since these components are made to order, design is not limited. We will discuss both the limitations and advantages of standard components in the next section.

Many prefinished materials are available. Among them are anodized aluminum for windows and panels, prefinished wall panels of wood and steel, and wood floors. We also find sprayed, baked, and veneered cabinets and vinyl and plastic coatings on many materials. The dollar saving in each case is only one of the factors to be considered. Other questions that must be answered are: will it speed the work, is design choice restricted, will the extra cost of careful handling and protection at the site outweigh the benefits? It is important to know how the parts will be joined. Prefinished, blind-nailed floors are really finished, while wallboard must often be taped and spackled and painted. Prefinishing simple joining systems has helped to increase the quantity and quality of do-it-yourself and self-help workmanship. The advantages of prefinishing are clear. This trend can be expected to accelerate.

The Introduction of Industrially Produced Components, Buildings, and Building Systems

As the manufacture of more of the elements of the building is moved off the site, a new kind of product, the industrially produced component, has appeared. Some of these, such as the finished window, the precast shower tray, and the package air conditioning unit are simple factory-made versions of traditional on-site operations. Others, such as stressed skin wall panels and prestressed concrete floor systems, are the products of new technologies.

In most construction, it is not the building, but its components which are industrial products. The designer is offered the opportunity of selecting from an increasingly broad, but nevertheless limited choice of components. Structural and nonstructural units, bath, kitchen, laundry, heating, storage, and enclosure are produced and can be combined with more or less ease in the finished building.

"Customerizing" the basic house—much as the automobile industry makes apparent variety by surface treatment, clip-ons, and changes in detail. (Courtesy of Building Systems Design, Inc.)

Installing premanufactured sidelights and windows. (Photo by Hedrich-Blessing.)

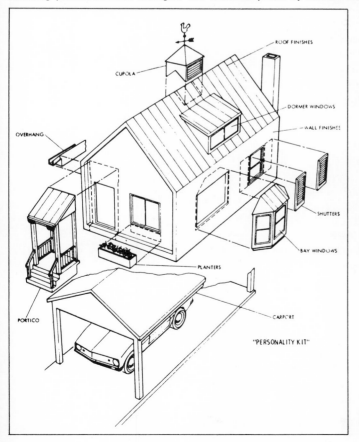

ROOF FINISHES

CUPOLA

DORMER WINDOWS

WALL FINISHES

OVERHANG

SHUTTERS

BAY WINDOWS

PLANTERS

PORTICO

CARPORT

"PERSONALITY KIT"

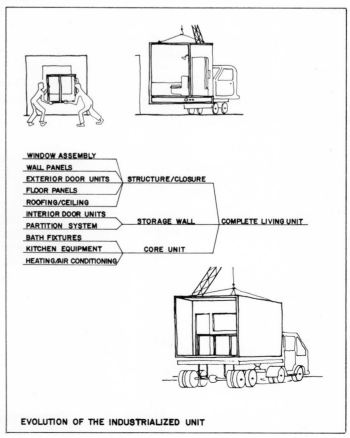

WINDOW ASSEMBLY
WALL PANELS
EXTERIOR DOOR UNITS ——— STRUCTURE/CLOSURE
FLOOR PANELS
ROOFING/CEILING
INTERIOR DOOR UNITS
PARTITION SYSTEM ——— STORAGE WALL ——— COMPLETE LIVING UNIT
BATH FIXTURES
KITCHEN EQUIPMENT ——— CORE UNIT
HEATING/AIR CONDITIONING

EVOLUTION OF THE INDUSTRIALIZED UNIT

THE WINDOW   The development of the construction of windows, from a number of operations on different materials by various crafts, to a single product selected from standard catalogues and ready for installation provides a clear example of the industrialization of a component.

In the traditional house, sash weights, pullies, sash guides, and trim were built into a rough opening in the wall. The frames were then milled and assembled, glass was cut and puttied into the sash, and this assembly was connected to the sash weight and fitted into the frame. Trim was added and hardware installed. Caulking, sanding, painting, and cleaning finished the window. Deliveries of lumber, hardware, glass, caulking putty, and paint had to be coordinated, then stored on the site, and, as weather permitted, carpenters, glazers, painters, and laborers were needed to work on the assembly.

The availability of milled stock for frames and sash and, later, preglazed sash, reduced the number of suppliers, deliveries, materials, and operations. Factory priming and prefinishing reduced them still further. Today, a large selection of finished window units made for fitting into the rough openings of typical wall constructions are available. The operation is reduced to one delivery and a simple installation. Some manufacturers are now manufacturing these finished window units in rough framed wall panels.

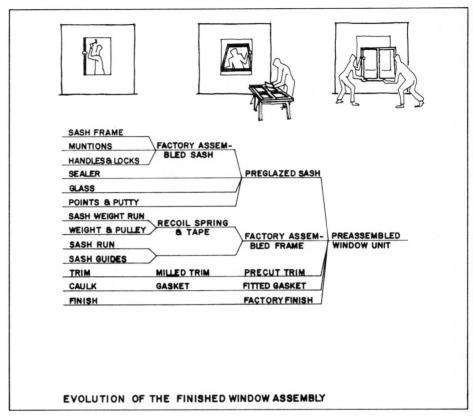

EVOLUTION OF THE FINISHED WINDOW ASSEMBLY

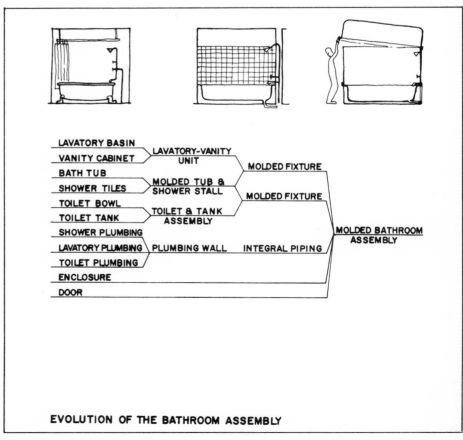

EVOLUTION OF THE BATHROOM ASSEMBLY

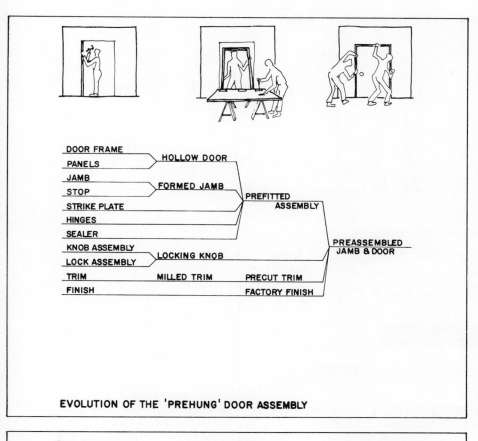

DOOR FRAME
PANELS → HOLLOW DOOR
JAMB
STOP → FORMED JAMB
STRIKE PLATE → PREFITTED ASSEMBLY
HINGES
SEALER
KNOB ASSEMBLY
LOCK ASSEMBLY → LOCKING KNOB → PREASSEMBLED JAMB & DOOR
TRIM → MILLED TRIM → PRECUT TRIM
FINISH → FACTORY FINISH

EVOLUTION OF THE 'PREHUNG' DOOR ASSEMBLY

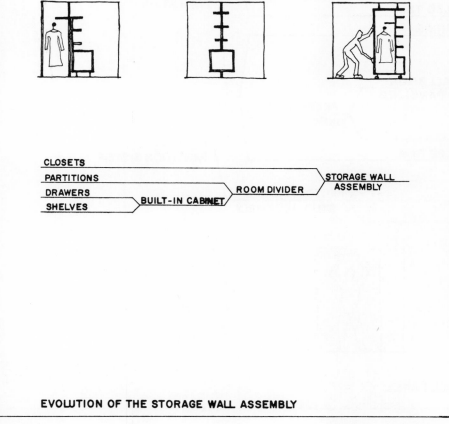

CLOSETS
PARTITIONS
DRAWERS → BUILT-IN CABINET → ROOM DIVIDER → STORAGE WALL ASSEMBLY
SHELVES

EVOLUTION OF THE STORAGE WALL ASSEMBLY

This approach to the manufacture of building components presents both problems and possibilities. Work is centralized. The material bypasses many local suppliers. It must be standardized to be useful nationally, and designed for effective packing and shipping. This results in a limited number of shapes, sizes, and finishes. Standardization restricts the expression of regional or community customs and practices and shipping may add large costs to the distribution of the product.

On the other hand, these developments increase value and reduce cost by moving labor off the site and into a shop. They provide more efficient working conditions, wider use of power equipment, tools and jigs, better material handling equipment, and freedom from uncertainties of weather.

They also create better opportunities for the design of the product and improve the assembly process. Product research and design can be concentrated, and quality control improved when cost is spread over a large number of units.

Large volume material and equipment purchases can be made which mean lower prices than those available to small builders. They also offer better opportunities to control purchases and to have products specifically tailored to needs. Management efficiency is improved through all stages of production.

New management skills of off-site producers have been a major development in the building industry. Putting the resources of industry to work on basic solutions (of The Window rather than involving the designer in a repetitious and superficial design for one window) can bring about major improvements in building products. This promises a reshaping of the components of homes and communities.

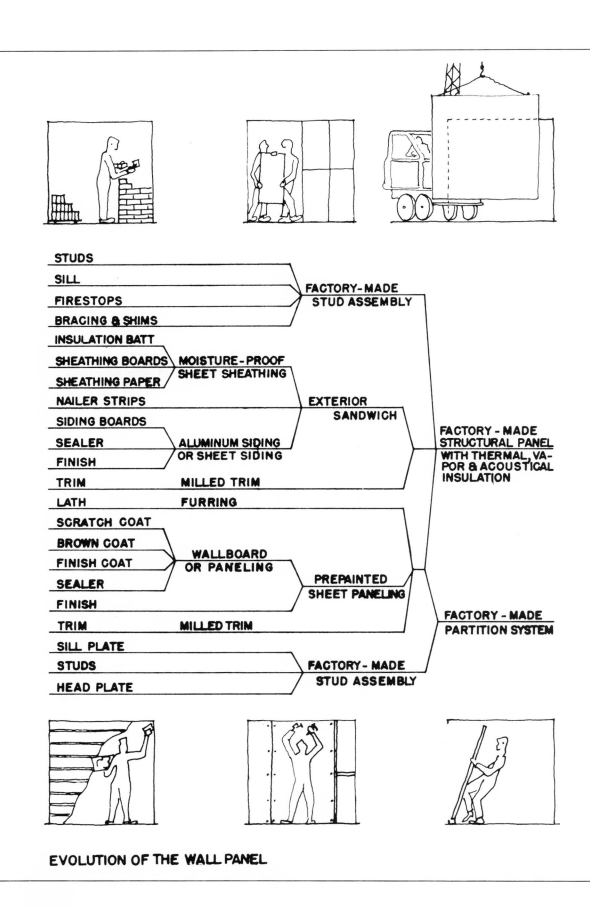

STUDS
SILL
FIRESTOPS
BRACING & SHIMS

FACTORY-MADE
STUD ASSEMBLY

INSULATION BATT
SHEATHING BOARDS — MOISTURE-PROOF
SHEATHING PAPER — SHEET SHEATHING
NAILER STRIPS
SIDING BOARDS
SEALER — ALUMINUM SIDING
FINISH — OR SHEET SIDING
TRIM — MILLED TRIM
LATH — FURRING

EXTERIOR
SANDWICH

FACTORY-MADE
STRUCTURAL PANEL
WITH THERMAL, VA-
POR & ACOUSTICAL
INSULATION

SCRATCH COAT
BROWN COAT
FINISH COAT — WALLBOARD
SEALER — OR PANELING
FINISH
TRIM — MILLED TRIM

PREPAINTED
SHEET PANELING

SILL PLATE
STUDS
HEAD PLATE

FACTORY-MADE
STUD ASSEMBLY

FACTORY-MADE
PARTITION SYSTEM

EVOLUTION OF THE WALL PANEL

A NEW FAMILY OF COMPONENTS

Many other components have evolved in much the same way as the finished window unit. Similar progressions can be traced for interior and exterior wall panels, doors, bathrooms, and storage units. Other widely used major components include trusses, stairs, heating and air conditioning packages, and kitchen equipment.

Those units which come under the regulation of building codes (such as stairs (wall panels, prefabricated plumbing walls) or which tend to invade the province of traditional crafts and businesses have had to fight for acceptance while those free of these constraints (such as cabinets and storage walls) have achieved acceptance more easily.

The large group of components which are factory-made and delivered to the building site ready for assembly include almost all the elements of the house. The dream of the pioneers of industrialization, to select standard parts from a catalogue, order them, and have them easily assembled into a finished building, is now possible. But it seems far from realization.

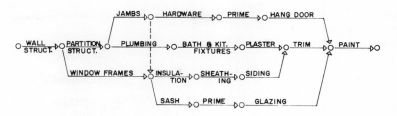

TRADITIONAL BUILDING

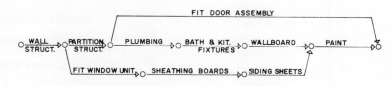

BUILDING WITH COMPONENTS

BUILDING WITH ASSEMBLIES OF COMPONENTS

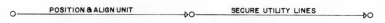

'PLUG-IN' BUILDING

THE REDUCTION IN ON-SITE BUILDING PROCESSES

As we begin to assemble components into larger units several problems arise. There must be a method of dimensional coordination before components can be interchangeable. This became apparent early in the development of industrialization. It led to great enthusiasm for modular planning. Modules proliferated—cubical modules, linear modules, structural modules, modular modules, modules based on the requirements of each product, each industry, and each and every building type. Architects even tried laying out drawings on a modular basis. But even in those industries where a single set of modular standards prevailed (such as wood-frame, masonry, or kitchen cabinets) a major problem remained at the interface of two components.

Where two pieces come together dimensionally, there must be a joint. Some industries have been able to arrive at generally accepted standards for these joints. Most domestic windows relate to the typical wall constructions and are sized to generally accepted modules and connections. But products with a general compatibility at the interface are rare.

There is no framework into which the manufacturer can fit. The custom builder, the tract developer, the materials manufacturer, distributor, or the individual user cannot take the lead. The large volume purchaser of buildings has not done so. Traditionally, only governments, municipal, state, or federal, have had this capability and they have only begun to explore it.

More recently new larger scale participants have appeared in the industry. These corporations, involved in every operation from land development and raw materials production to building finance and management, have the opportunity to make a framework which will maximize the support of manufactured components.

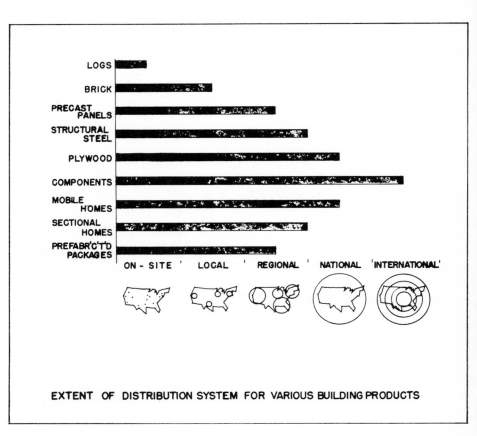

EXTENT OF DISTRIBUTION SYSTEM FOR VARIOUS BUILDING PRODUCTS

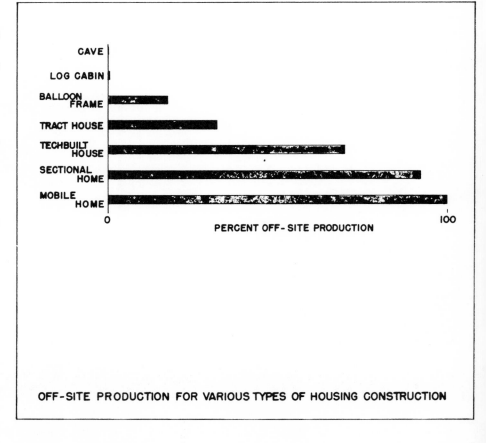

OFF-SITE PRODUCTION FOR VARIOUS TYPES OF HOUSING CONSTRUCTION

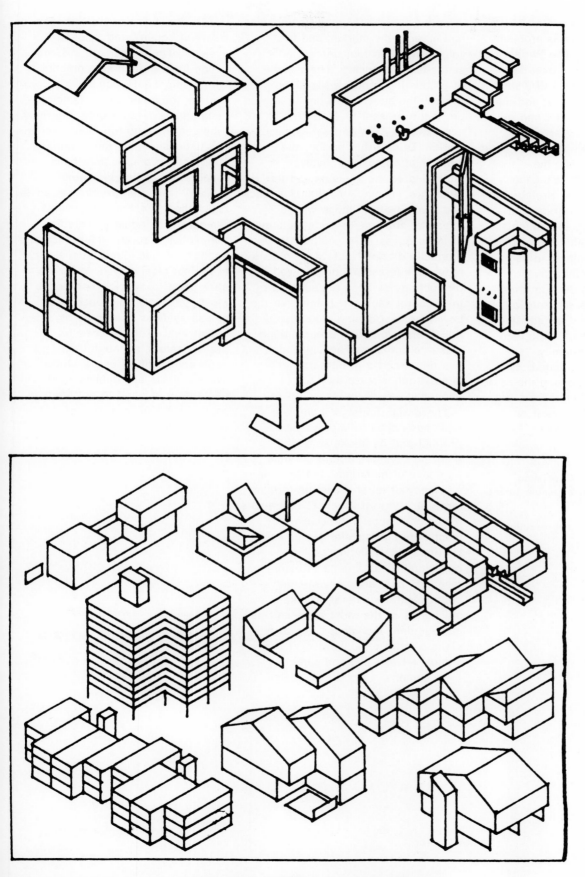

This "kit of parts" can be used to make this variety of buildings. (Courtesy of BSD, Inc.)

THE PREFABRICATOR   One of the first to find solutions to this problem was the prefabricator. The Prefab house literally ". . . came over on the Mayflower." Variations of it went west with the early settlers, and many examples of prefrabication can be found before the Civil War.

By accepting the responsibility for a total building design, with the objective of shipping a package ready for assembly, the prefabricator was forced to come to grips with all the problems of fitting and matching.

It is only recently that the "Home Manufacturer"* has emerged as an important part of the industry. Before World War II, despite great interest and a widespread conviction that prefabrication held the solution to building's problems,** less than one percent of single-family dwellings were prefabricated. With the emergency conditions of the war, this percentage increased, but still, less than fifteen percent of war emergency housing was prefabricated.

*Since 1958 the trade association has been called the Home Manufacturer's Association.

**See bibliography for some excellent surveys of the industry.

By the late 1940's many companies had entered the market, and the volume reached four percent of single-family housing. The volume of production continued to climb through the early 1950's until it leveled off at the present level of approximately ten percent of the market. During this period, the number of companies involved multiplied as the ideas caught the industry's imagination, then fell back and leveled off as those whose interests, abilities, or understanding of the process were inadequate gradually dropped out. More recently, renewed interest in industrialized production has been encouraged by the Federal sector. Projects like the Low Income Housing Demonstrations (LIHD) and Operation Breakthrough illustrate the kind of activity which has reinforced a great surge of interest only slowed by the economic sag of the early 1970's.

The prefabricator of complete buildings hopes to improve his product and its marketability by realizing savings through the bulk purchase of materials, and greater efficiency of labor crews performing large numbers of identical operations with more opportunity to use machinery and special equipment. He hopes to enjoy increasing opportunities to engage in planning, research, cost and performance control and, in general, to take advantage of the most advanced new management techniques. He also plans a more effective use of pro-motion, advertising, and sales organizations.

The prefabricator must choose between "open" and "closed" systems. The former are systems which have a general compatibility with components outside his own system; the latter are systems of components related only internally. While, in the long run, open systems are unquestionably more valuable, successful prefabricators have found that building lacks the industry-wide framework needed to make them function effectively. Almost every industry, including automotive, aircraft, electronics and appliances, has found it necessary to perfect closed systems before attempting to develop open ones. Most commonly both open and closed systems exist side by side.

The bulk of the successful prefabricators, although their approaches differ, use a closed system. Parts are dimensioned and joints are designed to go together easily in a limited series of configurations.

The prefabricated house is a factory-made house delivered to and assembled on the site. Prefabricators tend to use familiar materials and techniques. Most are of wood frame construction. They are often regionally or locally based. Some large lumberyards are involved in this work. Traditional crafts are used in the factory and at the site. Marketing arrangements, code, labor, builder, lender, and buyer acceptance have been in direct proportion to the house's similarity to conventional construction. Recently large manufacturers of lumber and land development organizations have shown interest in the prefab house because it provides a method of selling packaged materials in bulk at the same time as it provides a method of building on remote housing tracts where no building industry presently exists. Factors that have impeded the development of prefabricated houses are the often thoughtless use of new and unfamiliar materials, inflexibility of design, poor distribution systems, the lack of nationally or even regionally accepted codes, and the poor public image of the prefab as a cheap and badly built house. Perhaps the primary reason is that costs have not been significantly below those of houses built by high volume, well-organized, conventional builders.

Instant rehabilitation: wiring the service core. (Photo courtesy of U.S. Department of Housing and Urban Development.)

Hoisting the prefabricated core. (Photo courtesy of U.S. Department of Housing and Urban Development.)

Lowering into buildings. (Photo courtesy of U.S. Department of Housing and Urban Development.)

lustron homes*

Lustron Homes was organized prior to World World II by Carl Strandlund, an engineer inventor whose most notable accomplishment during that period of depression had been the raising of the gross income of the Oliver Farm Equipment Company from $20 million to $120 million per year. At the end of the war Strandlund was vice president of Chicago Vitreous Enamel Co.—a company which held patents on a process to porcelain enamel cold-rolled sheet steel as an alternative to the more expensive special enameling iron then commonly used. From steel washing machine finishes Chicago Vitreous moved into the production of porcelain enamel panels as a veneer for store fronts and hamburger stands.

Strandlund convinced Standard Oil of Indiana to use these panels as part of an all-steel gasoline station. But, in the press of Postwar material shortages, the government banned the proposal as non-essential. They suggested Strandlund produce houses instead. Three months after the government's proposal, early in 1946, Strandlund appeared in Washington with four hand trucks full of drawings and applications. He requested financing, a surplus war plant, and allocations of building steel. His appeal was to the Reconstruction Finance Corporation (RFC) under legislation passed in 1946 which authorized government loans to assist factory-built housing.

Strandlund found many friends, was backed by many supporters, among them Senator Ralph Flanders, a former engineer. The Senator supported the proposal before the Senate Banking Committee and assisted Strandlund in obtaining the necessary support. A loan of $15½ million was approved by the RFC 15 minutes before its emergency lending powers ceased on June 30, 1946. Subsequent extensions by the RFC would lead to additional loans, $10 million in the summer of 1948 and $7 million in February 1949. These were granted to protect the government's original commitment to the Lustron Homes project.

Strandlund was awarded a factory to work in as well. After the head of the government's housing program, an avid Lustron supporter, resigned when Lustron was not given the Chicago Dodge manufacturing plant, arrangements were made for the use of the former Curtiss-Wright fighter plane factory outside of Columbus, Ohio. Strandlund aimed high. Less than two years after the formation of the company, the plant was finished. Spread out over 23 acres, the plant could produce four houses an hour, almost 100 houses a day. The heart of the factory was a conveyor belt moving at 20 feet per minute. No wonder the Architectural Forum wrote:

"It is the first real demonstration of the seductive theory that houses can be turned out like automobiles. . . ."

*From a paper prepared at the University of California, Berkeley by Floyd E. Barwig.

Chicago Vitreous built a prototype Lustron Home in Hinsdale, Illinois in the first half of 1947 and then sold all rights to their porcelain enameling process to Strandlund. Using this prototype as part of an advertising campaign, Strandlund demonstrated the demand for Lustron Homes. In conjunction with his congressional support this convinced the Department of Commerce to allot 59,000 tons of steel to housing. Despite cries of favoritism, almost all of it was earmarked for Lustron.

The basis of Strandlund's plan was a 1,025 square-foot house built of mass produced steel parts. Using a host of automotive assembly line techniques including the conveyor, automatic assembly equipment, sheet steel stampings, wall, roof, and ceiling panels, and the porcelain enameling process acquired from Chicago Vitreous, a house made from mat-finished enameled steel panels over steel framing was produced. Innovation was found in almost every aspect of product and process. Many, now familiar, details appeared. Fiberglass insulation and rubber gasketing were used to eliminate the problem of thermal conductivity inherent in a steel house. Taking advantage of the steel ceiling, a radiant heating system based on a plenum above the ceiling was used. To attract buyers in the middle income one third of the housing market for which the Lustron Home was intended, built-in cabinets and storage walls, an automatic dishwasher, and a washing machine were included in the basic house.

All of the parts produced in the factory were loaded onto a special trailer designed to accommodate the 12½-ton house in such a manner that parts were unloaded at the site in the sequence in which they were needed for assembly. This allowed the trailer to function as an on-site warehouse until the house was completed. A tractor delivering one loaded trailer would return a nearby empty trailer to the factory for a new house. Problems with site assembly, especially of the cabinetwork, led to design changes and more factory assembly. More and more of the site work was moved to the factory, sub-assemblies were prepared. For example, the original gasketed 2' x 2' panels clipped to steel studs were replaced by floor-to-ceiling panels. Storage and plumbing walls were completed at the factory. From the initial 3,000 parts loaded onto each trailer, a group of 37 factory-built site-assembled elements evolved. In comparison, a similar sized wood frame house contained roughly 30,000 site-assembled parts. Eventually, the only major item of site work which remained was the preparation of the slab-on-grade which was its foundation and floor.

A comparable wood framed house required almost 1600 hours to assemble. Lustron Homes used 280 hours of factory work with an estimated 350 hours of site assembly. Assembly time was originally almost 1,000 hours when an unfamiliar crew began erection. With practice, time was reduced to 350 hours. Savings in labor more than made up for the cost of shiping a house within the large target area envisioned by Lustron. The West Coast was least accessible, but Strandlund had an idea of how to reach it. He began negotiating rates with the railroads to ship his trailers on flatcars in a manner similar to today's "piggy-back" shipping.

Lustron's head-on attack on production problems was not restricted to hardware. Early in the establishment of the Lustron Corporation, Strandlund conducted negotiations with international representatives of the AF of L, establishing the carpenters', plumbers', and electricians' jurisdiction over all factory and site processes at standard union wage rates. The prospect of year-round, indoor work as well as site work was agreeable to the unions.

While Lustron experienced little problem with organized labor during its existence, building codes were a continuing problem. Outmoded building codes would not accept copper plumbing and other aspects of Lustron. Rather than seeking total code revisions, variances were requested. Obtaining those variances was time and money consuming. The only advantage to Lustron was that as a standardized product, a variance obtained for one unit applied to all subsequent units built under the same jurisdiction. In the potentially large markets of Chicago and Detroit, Lustron never obtained variances. State and local FHA's added their requirements (in Tennessee, a door between the dining room and kitchen was required while other areas accepted Lustron's open plan), hindering standardization.

Lustron Corporation possessed the engineering know-how to cope with technical problems arising from their product and the process used to produce it. By the time of the company's demise they were preparing to market an improved luxury model, with a flexible floor plan and garage, designed in conjunction with architect Carl Koch. Strandlund envisioned developing a "used Lustron" market of basic parts and built-in furniture and appliances. But, for all his technical knowledge, and instincts, he was sadly lacking in financing and marketing ability. Strandlund assumed that the marketing of a technically sound product would work itself out.

As an example of lack of understanding in marketing, consider the Lustron bathtub. When bathtub suppliers would not lower their prices for bulk sales to Lustron, the company installed an 1,800-ton press to produce their own. They calculated that they could produce it at one third the price quoted by the suppliers. Unfortunately, Lustron only needed 40,000 bathtubs per year at the most, and the efficient production assumed in their figures required 120,000 units per year. The fact that no market existed for 80,000 out-size (5′ 1½″) bathtubs was not discovered until after the investment in equipment was made and production had started. The end product cost many times over the original suppliers' price.

Lustron Homes went on the market early in 1949. The general housing crisis had been partially resolved and a period of recession was following Postwar inflation. Variable land, foundation, and utility costs prevented the advertisement of a nationwide, standardized price. What was originally conceived as a $7,000 house became a $10-12,000 house. This was very close to the upper limit of the range in which Lustron was expecting to sell.

Financing a house from factory to site was a major problem. A dealer had to pay $6,000 before a trailer left the factory. Few dealers could afford to purchase a house or several houses until bank financing had paid them in advance. Some banks would not finance a prefabricated house while most would release money only in small payments, in accordance with their construction financing practices for conventional construction. Approvals of loans and all of the traditional practices of bank home financing could not produce mortgages as quickly as Lustron produced houses. Thus the dealer who could sell houses rapidly found himself in an impossible cash flow position. For each house he sold, $6,000 was tied up for the many months it took to close the mortgage.

To spur sales, dealership areas were reduced, bringing more capital into a given geographic area. An attempt was initiated to establish a nationwide acceptance corporation, modeled after the automotive industry, using private investment to develop the necessary starting capital. It was hoped that this would eliminate most of the interim financing problems for individual dealers and sidestep the issue of a Lustron house being classified as chattel while on the trailer and as real estate once erected, a problem which slowed many Lustron financing attempts.

Despite all of the problems of financing encountered by Lustron and difficulties with delivery due to a dispute with the firm doing all of Lustron's hauling, the popularity of the Lustron home persisted. Before the plant became fully operational, people in some areas arranged to make payments in esrow. Once operational, Lustron was selling while other comparably priced houses were empty. The low maintenance, forever-new look has been hypothesized for this attraction. But whatever the reason, a market for Lustron appears to have existed. For example, the military was contemplating the establishment of Lustron as their national standard for all single-family dwellings on military bases.) If a means to tap the one percent of the total housing market Strandlund aimed for had been found in time, Lustron might have succeeded.

All of the later financing attempts never had time to succeed. The last major loan from RFC to Lustron was actually a series of short-term loans given with a promise to consolidate them into one long-term note. Attempts at Congressional meddling with Lustron and dissatisfaction with Lustron's expensive ($100,000 per month in advertising) lobbying pressured RFC to foreclose in March 1950. Withdrawal of government support sealed Lustron's fate. Congressional investigations followed. President Truman ordered the plant reconverted to aircraft construction. Lustron's equipment was sold or scrapped.

It is impossible to evaluate definitively whether Lustron could have eventually overcome its marketing problems and become a successful manufacturer of mass-produced prefabricated homes. What is clear is that efforts of this sort must deal with a restructuring of every aspect of the housing process if they are to succeed.

A major reason for the difficulty in reducing costs is to be found in the relatively small portion of the total cost affected by the prefabricator. The costs of land, site development, foundations, maintenance, financing, and taxes are not changed through prefabrication. The increasingly large percentage of house costs represented by hardware, equipment, appliances, and finished components represent fixed costs regardless of construction technique. Again, many prefabricated houses are not complete packages. They are no more than structure and enclosure (shells) and require the installation of subsystems and finishes at the site. The failure of many of the early prefabrication operations such as the "Lustron House" illustrates most of the points made above. As a result of this experience, the industry has developed along a few mixed lines:

1. The complete housing package is delivered in parts and assembled on the site. (Package Builders)

2. The finished building in one or more sections is set down on the site. (The Sectional Home Manufacturer)

3. Prefabrication of part of the building, usually the structure enclosure system, occurs with conventional finishing. (The Prefabricator)

4. A building system is used.

The first two of these approaches are variations on a single theme which balance their relative advantages and disadvantages. Although the first method continues to provide a large number of houses each year, the second, as represented by the sectionalized house and the mobile home, has grown to absorb the great bulk of the single-family, low-cost home market. The last two approaches, modified conventional housing and system building, represent different degrees of sophistication applied to the same solution.

Most large-scale builders fall into the third category. They continue to use on-site labor to provide flexibility and local contacts. They limit their use of components, industry prefabrication, and even their own shop fabrication to areas in which these products and techniques can make significant improvements. They make wide use of prefabricated structure-enclosure systems, such as the steel frame and curtain wall or the wood truss and tilt-up wall panels, to enclose the building rapidly. Package heating systems and unit air conditioners, which eliminate time-consuming mechanical operations and are generally accepted by labor, building codes, and the user, are also widely used.

At the same time, they continue to make connections and finish surfaces with conventional crafts and skills.

The precut house, a package containing cut and shaped material, is a good example of the application of prefabrication to one "subsystem" of building. It might be described as an assembly of independent, non-compatible systems. Within each subsystem, problems are carefully solved. But they are solved only with regard to that subsystem. The final assembly will reflect the problem of their interfaces. We will find holes cut in the structure of finished surfaces, exposed pipes and wires, differential expansion at joints, and colors that do not quite match. At present, the greatest part of an architect's time and energy, as well as that of the engineer, builder, and building inspector, is taken up with these problems of incompatible interfaces.

Progression from an assembly of unrelated parts to dimensional coordination within narrow limits was the basis for the development of the building system. The concept of a building system is directly related to the parallel developments of "general systems theory" and a "systems approach" to complex problems. This attitude views problems as interrelated sets of interdependent parts working together for the overall objective of the whole. It offers the possibility of significant improvement in the construction of buildings.

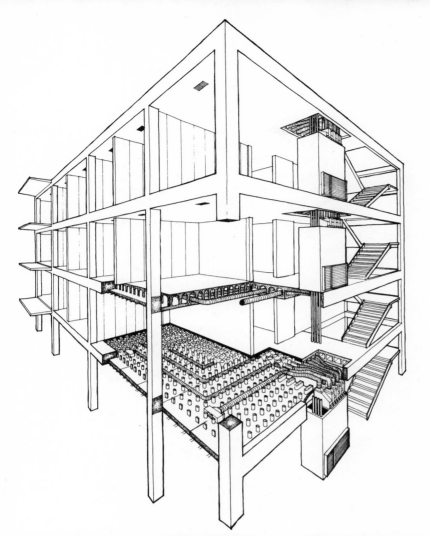

THE BUILDING SYSTEM   The building system has been called a "kit of parts." It consists of a group of components and subsystems which can be combined in a great variety of configurations to provide a large number of solutions to any given problem. At one end, it is based on the belief that mass-production processes are best utilized when a wide variety of designs can be developed from a minimum of parts. At the other extreme, it realizes the volume of production necessary to research the user requirements and the performance characteristics of these components as well as the design, manufacture, and distribution of them is so complex that it requires a reorganization of the market. The form of the industry and its context will be affected by this reorganization.

Mechanical equipment integrated into the building system. University Residential Building System.

The concept of a building system is analogous to the early printing press. Once the alphabet and rules are invented there is no limit to what can be written with the system. (Source: *Men, Machines, and History,* International Publishers, New York.)

The value of a building system lies in the characteristics of its elements, the number of them compatible within the system, the operations required to join them, and the versatility of their joinery. Obviously, the development of a series of national and international open systems would be of great value to manufacturers, designers, builders, and users.

It should be clear that the crucial qualities of a good system lie in the compatibility of component interfaces. The typical flat slab, reinforced concrete, brick-faced apartment building is an open system. A great number of building components can be used in it. However, lack of organized components compatibility limits its effectiveness.

One of the first, and certainly one of the most influential building systems was the "Techbuilt House." Techbuilt introduced a family of house components which included most of the structure, wall, and floor construction, a variety of window and door elements, and materials and finishes coordinated both dimensionally and physically.

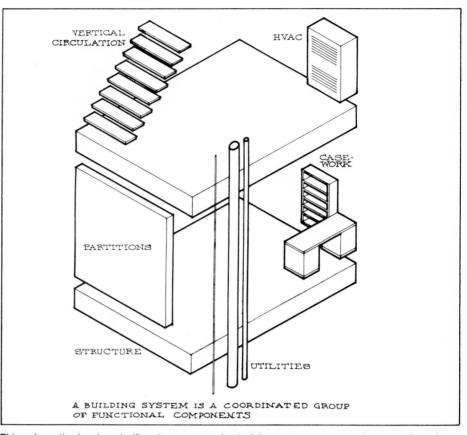

A BUILDING SYSTEM IS A COORDINATED GROUP OF FUNCTIONAL COMPONENTS

This schematic drawing clarifies the concept of a building system as a set of precoordinated components. (Courtesy of BSD, Inc.)

Hercules, Inc.

PROPOSER

Hercules, Inc., Wilmington, Delaware

AFFILIATES

Hercoform Marketing, Inc. (formerly Modular Structures, Inc.), Design, Marketing; Armstrong and Salomonsky, Architects; Harlan, Betke & Meyers, Financing Methods; University of Utah, Site Planning

Two systems of factory-completed volumetric modules, using conventional materials and mass production fabrication techniques, are the central thrust of this proposal. The modules are a maximum of 12 ft. wide, 11 ft. high, and up to 60 ft. long, and are joined together onsite. A variety of architectural types, with price ranges based on choices of components and materials, as well as living space and siting adaptabilities, is possible through multiple configurations of the modules.

The proposed multifamily high-rise structure utilizes a new concept of finished steel wall partitions integral

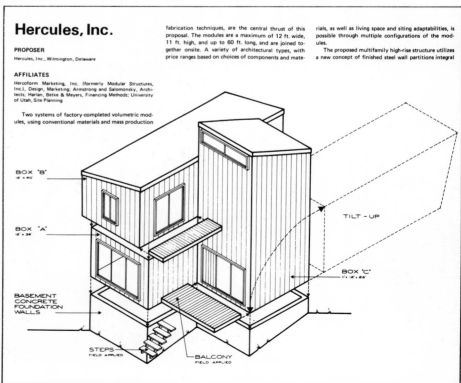

Variations on the way in which boxes can be used as a new large-scale, building element. (Courtesy of Hercules, Inc., Wilmington, Del.)

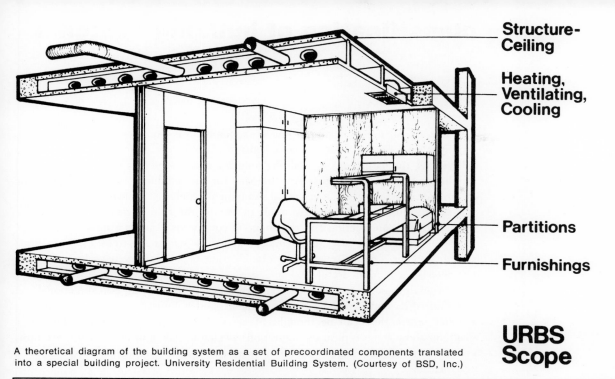

Structure-Ceiling

Heating, Ventilating, Cooling

Partitions

Furnishings

A theoretical diagram of the building system as a set of precoordinated components translated into a special building project. University Residential Building System. (Courtesy of BSD, Inc.)

URBS Scope

Mechanical equipment integration in the Academic Building System. (Courtesy of BSD, Inc.)

classification of building systems

While the structure is simply one of a number of subsystems which form buildings, and while in cost and complexity it is rarely the most significant of the subsystems, the nature of our building industry makes structure central to any building system. The structure sets the pace for the building, enclosing, supporting or providing stability for mechanical equipment, enclosure, finishes, and furnishings. Just as the carpenter tends to assume the role of general contractor in small house construction and the concrete contractor assumes a similar role in high-rise housing, the structural concept generally sets the pattern of the systems builder. For this reason, the classification of building systems by structural characteristics is most useful.

In general, these systems can be considered as one directional, two directional, and three directional; that is, as linear, planar, and volumetric systems. In more familiar terms, they can be thought of as: skeletons, slabs, and boxes. The diagrams show some typical configurations—skeleton, slab, and box systems are now common in the full range of building materials, wood, concrete, metals, and plastics.

These approaches cannot be ranked on an absolute scale of quality or characterized as generally better or worse. Each, however, has characteristics which make it more or less appropriate to specific situations. As we move from skeleton to box systems, we tend to trade off flexibility for the advantages of increased factory production.

A sectional, or box, unit arrives at the site with little more than utility hookups and site work to be done. Thus it can take great advantage of the economies of the factory. But the box is a quite limited planning unit; dimensions are fixed by transport requirements, and plan variation by the limited number of permutations and combinations of the few box types. Finish and detail design is set at the factory for the full range of production.

At the opposite end of the scale, the skeleton allows much more planning freedom and individual input, but it is at the expense of the economies of factory assembly. These tradeoffs and the choice of system, then, are related to building type (a motel can use a box more easily than an apartment house), program (those planning housing for large families with low income will value the planning freedom of a skeleton while senior citizen housing may not suffer from the restriction of the box), and expectations of the user.

To date, the value of the planning freedom and possibility for individual variation has not been great enough for skeleton systems to make serious headway in housing. Box systems and their cost reduction have been powerful enough to make major inroads in the low-rise residential area, while concrete panel systems with higher costs but more spatial variety can compete in the high density housing market, where the requirements of strength, lateral stability, insulation, and fire protection recognize the value of the more expensive technique.

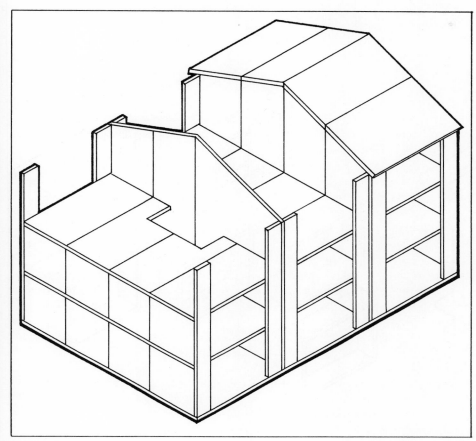

Panel system.

It brought with it a new group of market innovations in dealerships, franchised builders, national advertising, and an architectural consulting service. It has many advantages over conventional construction. The owner is able to plan his own house on a modular grid, and select components and finishes from a catalogue with professional design assistance. The contractor can quickly price the package and give a firm estimate of costs. Erection is quick and easy with the advantages of a simplified foundation system, off-site production, erection by local craftsmen, and the use of familiar tools and techniques. These advantages, particularly the time and money savings in the design-estimate-contract stage, have brought other house systems into the field. These systems have been particularly successful in vacation areas, areas of sudden growth or extreme climate as well as those of limited accessibility. Short building seasons, limited supplies of local labor, builders, and materials, minimum coordination and shipping, and the incentive to "finish in time for the season" make these building systems even more attractive.

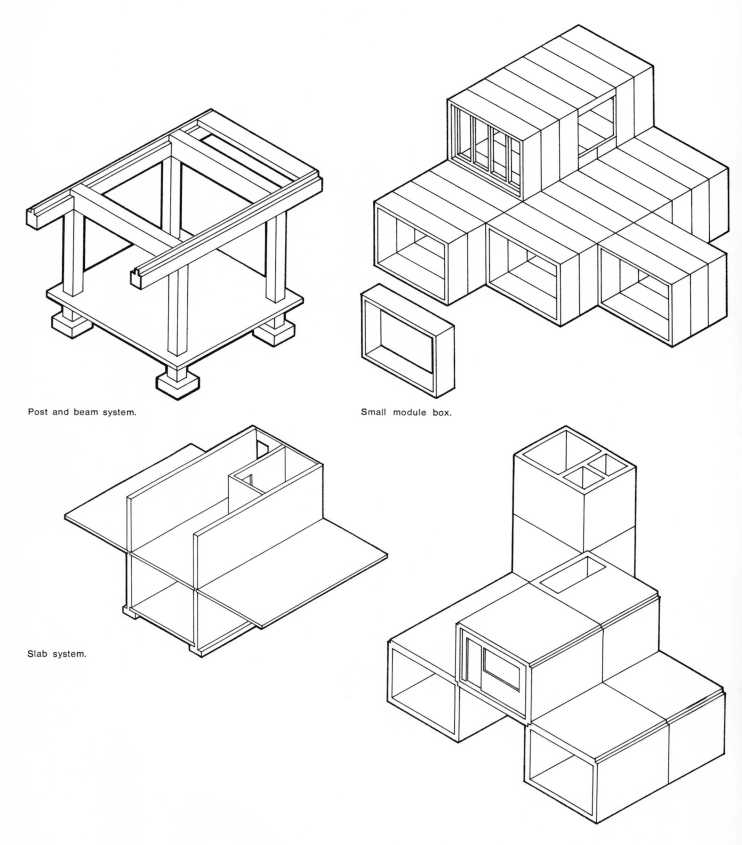

Post and beam system.

Small module box.

Slab system.

Intermediate box module.

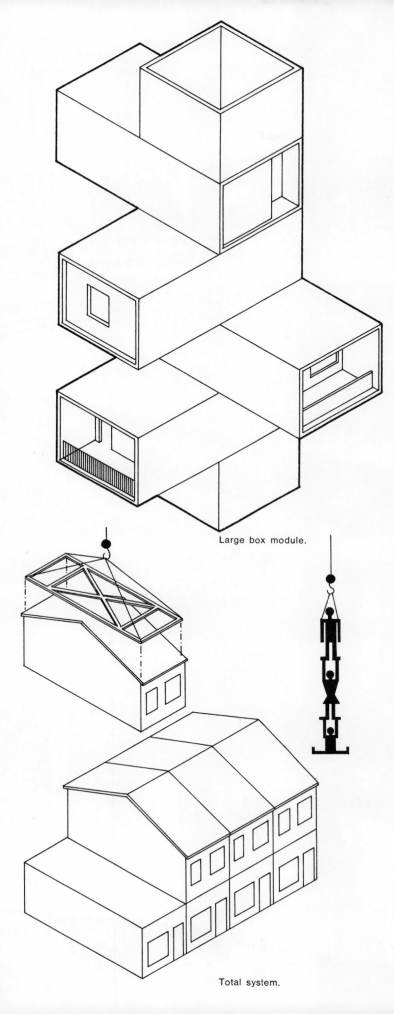

Large box module.

Total system.

The enormous shortage of housing, skilled labor, and materials in Europe as a result of World War II led to a change in scale of the development of housing systems there. European systems for the most part are based on the use of concrete elements. These are relatively inexpensive, locally available, and provide the fire protection, sound insulation, and low maintenance characteristics necessary in high density buildings. Usually, a single company takes full responsibility for the structure, selection of materials, design and erection. Technical approaches vary from factory-produced components to finished, room-size boxes. Construction varies from factory production to on-site shop precasting to mechanized in-place casting. European systems have many elements in common. They attempt to integrate the building's subsystems into one overall system including structure and enclosure with the electrical and mechanical systems. A variety of plan, material and finish can be quickly planned and erected within rigid budget controls. Fewer site workers with new assembly skills are used, offering year-round, indoor work under modern factory conditions.

The new building systems technology comes most clearly into conflict with traditional labor practices. Without question, labor is seriously affected. More and more of the work is moved off the site and into factories. New material, new tools, skills, and attitudes on the part of labor are involved. The work required to produce a given unit of construction is decreased. A recent study shows that the number of man-hours spent by European builders to produce a given unit of housing has been cut in half by the use of system building. Recent American experiments show that the level of skill required by work crews is considerably lower than that of conventional construction; new unskilled workers can be introduced where craftsmen were once required.

The pressure on craft unions is obvious. Better working conditions, the promise of more working days each year, higher pay for productivity, and better safety records attract the individual worker and the industrial unions. The new components cut across traditional trade boundaries and threaten craft union classifications. The enormous building program which must be undertaken to satisfy world need obviously cannot be met by traditional crafts. However, even with more effective industrialization there will continue to be more than enough work for skilled craftsmen. The labor for the industrialized housing industry will have to come from outside the traditional trade unions.

(1) The quest for precise elements with smooth surfaces has led to the use of costly steel moulds, thus guaranteeing close tolerances, perfect edges, and clean surfaces. Furthermore, they permit the construction of large panels, which are increasingly in demand here and abroad. Note hand labor mixed with mechanized forms and lifting equipment.

(2) The outer surface can be finished with textured stucco of concrete with exposed aggregate. The traditional finishing operations are moved indoors.

(3) Facade elements are produced on large steel cables. They consist of an outer (10 cm thick) and an inner (7 cm thick) concrete panel separated by an 4-cm insulating layer of styropor. Note the hand labor involved. Volume of production is not great, but enough to have special sizes and shapes of insulation made.

(4) All ceiling elements and supporting and separating walls are produced in vertical mould batteries. The whole electrical installation and the door frames are inserted in the moulds, together with the cut-outs for the heating installation.

(5) The elements are stored near the factory before being transported to the various sites.

(6) Ten-ton cranes lift the elements in place ► for mounting.

(7) Unloading panels at the site: the thick ► piece to the right is an extension panel that is insulated; the thin pieces are for the nonbearing walls.

(8) On-site delivery follows a predetermined plan. Weight and dimensions of the elements are limited in order to facilitate transport on roads and railroads. Trucks are modified to carry safely a number of panels. The location of each piece is carefully planned to speed erection and eliminate duplication of movements.

The producer also finds himself pressured for change. Large vertical building organizations are one result of this pressure. Another, which comes from the nature of large-scale industrial operations, is the increasing use of careful scheduling and programming to organize and manage the work. A third is the tendency to build a number of dispersed plants rather than centralized "superplants."

An interesting sidelight to organized labor's reputation as a roadblock to progress is found in the role of the subcontractor. Labor finds that it can move to the factory and continue to be productive and well-paid while practicing traditional skills in a new context. However the new combined products such as walls, rooms, and entire dwellings have replaced plaster, wires, and carpentry as separate products. They eliminate the need for the trade specialties of the subcontractor. Subcontractors, on the other hand, tend to have a strong local base. They are influential in the politics and business of their communities. In defending their traditional roles they have been most effective roadblocks to innovation.

The weight, bulk, and brittle nature of concrete as well as the general availability of skills and materials have encouraged a regional distribution of the production facilities rather than centralized concentrations of concrete fabricators. The relative low cost of concrete working equipment compared to that for rolling steel or extruding aluminum makes this distribution feasible.

We find systems such as the Danish Larsen-Nielson and Jesperson systems, the French Balency and Tracoba, the British Bison, and several Russian systems operating plants through licensing agreements in many parts of the world. Most of the major European systems are now represented in the United States and Canada. Several have completed projects here.

The technical sophistication which had developed with integrated building units has seen changes in all the institutions connected with building. The manufacturer has become much more involved with the design and construction of projects. As communities undertake projects of larger scale, they find it possible to allocate funds for research into user requirements and performance criteria. As work tends to be bid on a "performance" rather than "specification" basis, systems based upon different materials and principles compete against each other. Manufacturers of smaller building components coordinate their products to compete for use in the building system, and building develops variety within an understandable framework.

The role of the designer is changed. He has the time and the resources to study basic problems. For example, he can view homes not as preconceived wall, roof, and window complexes, but as systems to provide shelter and control environment. There is also the opportunity to spend more time on architectural and planning problems, and less on repetitious detailing and transmitting instructions to the builder.

◄ (9) The size of the elements is determined by the size of the respective rooms. The ceiling elements (16 cm thick) rest on supporting walls (14 cm thick); facade elements carry no structural loads. The element joints ensure adequate dilation.

(10) Building with elements independent of weather conditions.

◄ (11) Special rigs permit lowering of whole sections of the stairs to their final positions.

(12) Finishing operations follow directly after mounting of elements.

Perhaps the most significant recent experiment in building was that of the School Construction Systems Development (SCSD). It centered around the creation of a framework to organize the following elements: (1) The formation of a large market; (2) The use of the resources of this new market or client, for the development of user requirements and then performance specifications; (3) The encouragement of industry's participation in the development of components and systems and industry's attempt to develop new products to meet these specifications with the new market held out as a prize.

The SCSD project used a "systems approach" in which the development of a building system was a component of the solution.*

*See illustrations for more on SCSD.

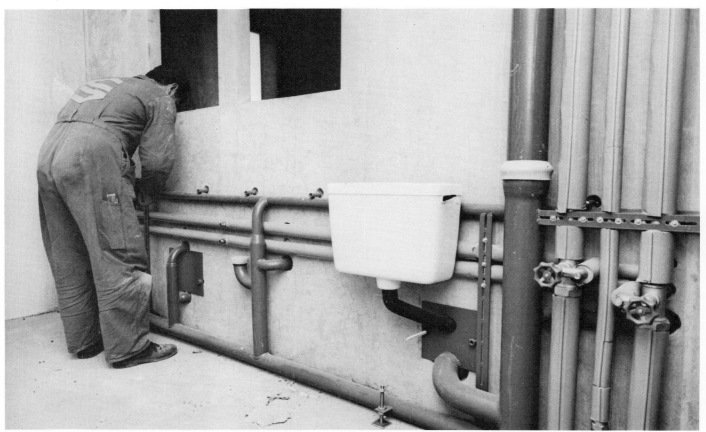

SCSD

The School Component Systems Development (SCSD) was organized in California in 1961 with Ezra Ehrenkrantz as Project Architect.

Thirteen of the state's school districts planning twenty-two school projects with an aggregate budget of $30 million joined together. Aided by a grant from the Ford Foundation's Educational Facilities Laboratories, user requirements were analyzed, performance specifications were prepared, and bids were requested on four compatible subsystems (structure, lighting and ceiling, partitions, and air conditioning). The specifications called for each manufacturer to design components meeting the performance requirements, and compatible with the others but bid separately. The system components comprised about 50% of the total building. Thus, while the architects who designed the individual buildings were required to use the four SCSD subsystems, they were free to adapt the building to the site and to design the exterior using conventional materials and constructional methods.

Industry showed great interest in this project. The stakes were high. The performance specification was carefully designed and promised a market much wider than the original 22 schools while the volume guaranteed by the project reduced the risk involved in entry. A group of excellent proposals were received and, in 1965, a contract was awarded to a group consisting of the Inland Steel Products Co. for the structure, lighting and ceiling; Lennox Industries for heating and cooling; and E. F. Hauserman Co. and Hough Manufacturing Co. for partitions. The excellent system design by architect Robinson Ward and an elegant prototype, built in Palo Alto, have done much to spread interest in the project. The schools have now been in use for several years. They have received wide acclaim and they have demonstrated a wide range of architectural expression.

While the costs were not significantly lower than schools built traditionally, the SCSD schools do exhibit many valuable qualities not found in usual school construction. Despite the experimental nature of the program, they have a record of quick planning and erection. The long spans called for great plan flexibility and the high quality of the components are a mark of the success of the program. While the Inland Steel Products Co. has discontinued production of their part of the system, a group of subsystems not included in the original contract award (such as the structural systems by Butler Manufacturing Co., Macomber, Inc., and Rheem/Dudley) have found a market for their product and sufficient compatibility with various other subsystems to exploit this market successfully. The Lennox HVAC Rooftop Unit has revolutionized the mechanical technology used in California schools and greatly increased Lennox as a force in the market.

◄ (13) The joints of the elements form a visible geometric pattern on the outside walls. This is typical use of exterior wall panels in a Swiss housing unit. (These photos are courtesy of Bruno Kirchgraber-Lang, Zurich, Switzerland.)

◄ (14) The sanitary installations consist of prefabricated sections which can be put into place and then joined up.

The photos above and on the previous page are courtesy of Building Systems Development, Inc.

The Use of Industrial Methods to Produce Products, Components, Assemblies, and Finished Units of Increasingly Larger Scale

Most people who visited Montreal's Expo '67 felt that they had seen the city of the future in "Habitat." A vision was projected in the tradition of the great World's Fairs of the last century. It was a vision of a city of manufactured houses, on racks or stacks, plugged into a framework, slid into place like drawers or set like giant bricks, tilted off trucks, lifted by cranes or helicopters. It was a vision of complete apartments coming off an assembly line to be shipped across the country by truck, train, or airplane; a vision of housing units that would be used, exchanged, or traded in for new ones. Habitat seemed to encourage all the fantasies we have ever had of industrialized clip-on, plug-in metamorphic cities.

Certainly the enormous attention given Habitat proves that there is a great interest in such ideas. The dream of a factory-finished, home-size building component is not a new one. In fact, it is just such a unit, the mobile home, which has exploded on the American market. Today it accounts for about one-third of the total, single family, nonfarm housing market. More than six million people live in these more or less mobile units.

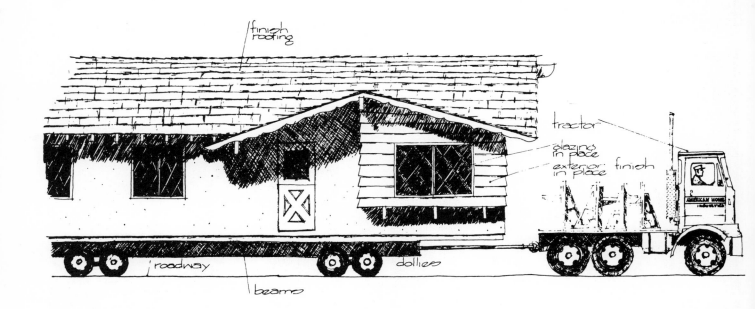

(Right) Habitat. (Photos courtesy of Expo Corporation.)

The mobile home is the most spectacular innovation in building today. It has developed from two directions. One is the increase in scale of factory-made components from a wall, to room, to a living unit and the other is the application of automobile production methods to the construction of wood frame houses.

As the unit size and degree of factory finish increase, so do the economies of factory production. But at the same time, increased size limits the possibility of variation through combination of parts and limits shipping feasibility. The number of units in the two most well-known examples of large scale buildings, Habitat and the San Antonio Hilton, was not large enough to make use of mass-production techniques of any consequence. The units produced were too bulky to move for any appreciable distance. The fabrication of Habitat, for example, took place on the site. Special carrying and lifting devices were employed to move and lift the finished units into place. The process, in fact, moved the factory to the site.

This technique is related to earlier experiments by IBEC and Le Tourneau. In the late 1940's these groups developed processes which involved moving a form around the site and the casting of one story units in place. It is also related to the "Jack-Block" and "Lift-Slab" systems of raising finished or semifinished floors into place, and to the more recent "tunnel form" systems which use sophisticated, apartment-size forms to cast high-rise structures in place.

The similarity to traditional construction is obvious. Workmen place reinforcing, wiring, and plumbing, install doors and windows, paint and finish much as they would in a well-organized housing development. But there are advantages to treating the site as a factory. Much of the work is on the ground rather than in the air. There are savings in scaffolding and framework. Other economies result from repetition, large volume, and the lifting of only the material which is to remain as part of the building. While no significant cost reduction can be claimed for these operations, they tend to speed construction, make work possible in bad weather, and require fewer of some scarce craft skills.

The argument that more units would have lowered Habitat's cost to the point of competition with conventional construction costs is deceptive. Of course, the costs of special equipment could have been distributed among more units, but such a large, guaranteed market would also have allowed the conventional builder to make many economies.

The primary argument for the use of these techniques is their speed of erection, quality control, and the reduction of craft skills required. This was the reason for its use in San Antonio. The great value of Habitat has nothing to do with low-cost housing, or perhaps, even with industrialization. Its value lies instead in the scale of its parts and in the architectural possibilities suggested by the rich level of variety in urban life it proposes.

RUSSIAN BOXES   In the U.S.S.R., two large-scale box systems have been successfully used. In one of these, the units are standardized in the form of five boxes: stair boxes, two types of kitchen and bathroom boxes, and two types of living-bedroom units. These boxes are roughly eighteen feet long by nine

feet high and ten feet wide weighing four to five tons. By varying the combination of elements, one, two, three, and four room apartments have been made. Assembly line production in regional factories is facilitated by the acceptance of a limited number of prototypes and of dimensions derived from transporation requirements.

In a second system using more massive boxes (33 feet long by 10½ feet wide and nine feet high and weighing from eighteen to thirty tons) two room elements are cast. These are lifted into place by special gantry cranes. In both the first and second system the boxes are finished, windows glazed, floors covered, walls painted, and all equipment installed at the factory.

The large volume and small number of variations make it possible to use automatic casting beds, prestressing, steam curing, and in-shop conveyor belts. Four story buildings with 45 apartments are erected in two months. It takes one and one-half months for the foundation. Only two weeks are required to set and connect the boxes. There are significant savings in such a system. The elements take on the characteristics of bricks in a new and larger urban scale. The design potential then becomes the creation of elements with the variety of possible combinations of a brick. While this approach was favored in the early Soviet rush to catch up with Postwar demand, much of their present production has switched to the more flexible panel systems. Perhaps this indicates a conflict between the inflexibility of box systems and the rising expectations of the Russian consumer.

These Russian boxes, though made of concrete rather than wood and metal, have many of the characteristics of the newest developments in the mobile home industry.

Precast housing boxes in Moscow. (Photo by Forrest Wilson.)

THE MOBLIE HOME INDUSTRY
Originally known as trailers, trailer-coaches, or caravans, mobile homes were generally used as vacation homes during the shaping of the industry in the 1930's. At that time they accounted for an insignificant part of the housing supply.

Although some experimentation with trailers was undertaken by the TVA, it was World War II that saw the crucial turning point for the industry. The population became more mobile as workers moved to the locations of newly established war industries. Military bases and new industrial communities were quickly formed and population increased while new housing construction was at a standstill. The trailer appeared to be the best available "instant" housing for industrial workers, families of the military, and the government's emergency housing needs. The housing shortage following the war maintained this pressure for growth.

As the Postwar housing shortage diminished, the continuing demand for trailers indicated that trailer inhabitants considered these units more than makeshift housing. For many people, the trailer had become a positive solution to housing needs. The trailer-coach manufacturers began to see themselves as involved in housing and "The Mobile Home" industry emerged.

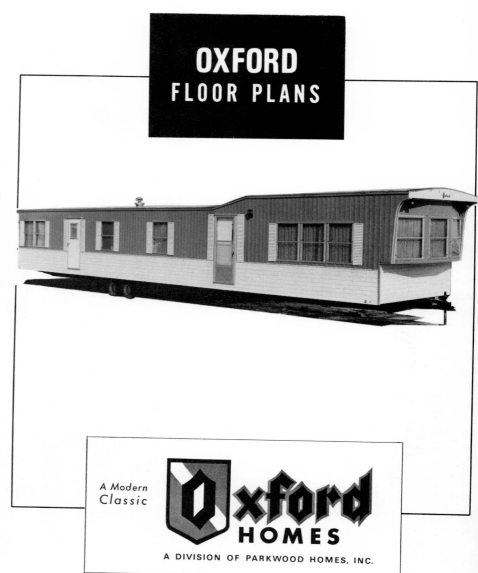

OXFORD FLOOR PLANS

A Modern Classic Oxford HOMES
A DIVISION OF PARKWOOD HOMES, INC.

Photo courtesy of Oxford Homes, Division of Parkwood Homes, Inc.

The mobile home is defined by the Mobile Home Manufacturers Association as ". . . a movable or portable dwelling constructed to be towed on its own chassis, connected to utilities, and designed without a permanent foundation for year-round living. It can consist of one or more units that can be folded, collapsed, or telescoped when towed and expanded later for additional capacity including two or more units, separately towable but designed to be joined into one integral unit, capable of being again separated into the components for repeated towing." It is a fully factory fabricated home that is mobile in the sense that it can be moved, but which increasingly becomes permanently attached to a site. The average mobile home stays in one spot for years. MHMA estimates that 70% of the two million mobile homes produced since World War II have been used for permanent or primary housing.

Mobile home factories are located in many parts of the country, but their greatest concentration, about 30% of the total production, is in the Midwest, especially in Ohio, Indiana, and Illinois. This area centered around Eckhart, Indiana has been called the "Prefab Belt" because of its concentration of producers of industrialized housing. It is more than a coincidence that it is close to the center of the auto industry. Most factories work on an assembly line system, moving the product through a series of stations where operations are successively performed and where preassambled components and subsystems are installed.

WESTERN (or PLATFORM) FRAMING

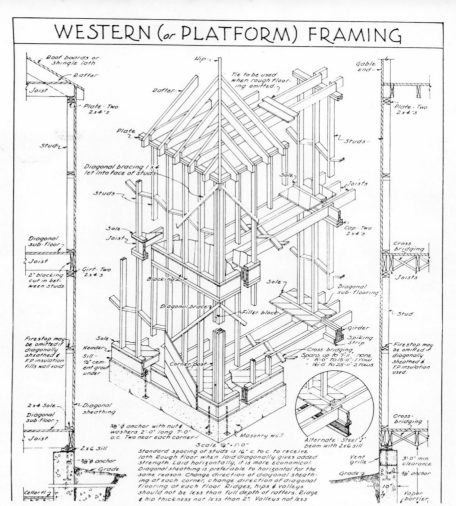

Platform framing: compare this with the construction of mobile and sectional homes. With platform framing as opposed to balloon framing, the stage was set for prefabrication of walls and modules. (Source: *Graphic Standards* by Ramsey and Sleeper.)

BALLOON FRAMING

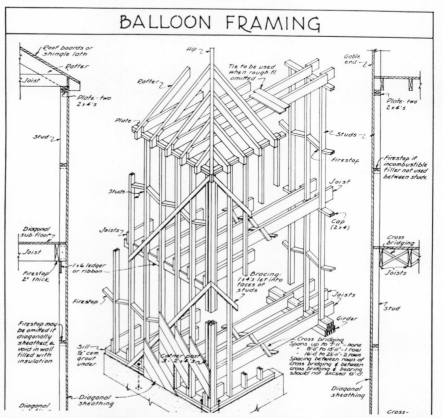

Balloon framing: compare this with the more recent platform framing to see how the form evolved as a response to changing tools, skills, and standards in the housing industry. (Source: *Graphic Standards* by Ramsey and Sleeper.)

Photo courtesy of Signode Corporation, Chicago, Illinois.

Mobile home construction is basically wood frame on a steel chassis. Most units use metal roofing and siding. New units are sold fully equipped with appliances, furniture, draperies, carpet, and occasionally, even light fixtures. Linen and silverware are sometimes included. The quality and low cost of the product are the result of savings inherent in volume purchases and a production process which uses year-round labor working indoors. Special equipment, materials, tools, and jigs are used and specialized labor employed. Research is conducted and combined with careful management and aggressive marketing.

The worker in the mobile home plant may perform the same operation as the on-site craftsman, but he performs it under better conditions, with better tools, and more specialized experience.

The trades, shipments of materials, components, and subsystems are better coordinated, thus eliminating costly delays, patching, and the complex interweaving of traditional crafts. These procedures, while not yet automated to the degree found in the automobile industry, are suited to the volume of production and the materials used, and are compatible with the low investment in special equipment which is a prerequisite for flexible design and easy model variation.

As more and better components become available, and as the larger manuafcturers are able to bring more and more complete subsystems to the assembly line, the efficiency of production can be expected to improve.

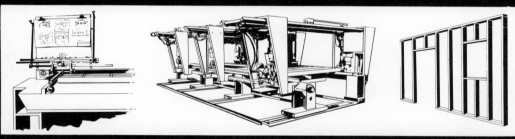

Photos courtesy of Dura-Built Metal Products, Inc.

Over the years the scale of mobile homes has grown considerably. Widths have increased from at first 8, to 10 to 12 and occasionally 14 feet. Lengths have grown from 30 to 40, 50, and as long as 60 feet. To make them competitive in the permanent house market, mobile homes now feature double widths, foldouts, telescoping sections, and additions available at the site. At the same time, efficiencies and the compact design which shipping imposes on the size of the product have kept prices significantly lower than those of conventional houses.

Eight to twelve dollars per square foot, depending upon the appliances, fixtures, and furnishings, is the approximate range. Ten dollars per square foot is the average. The average price for an unfurnished house, conventionally constructed, is about fifteen dollars per square foot. According to the U. S. Department of Commerce Census data, in 1969, over 90% of all single family homes sold for less than $15,000 were mobile homes.

Their low first cost, immediate availability, automobile-type financing, easy maintenance, organized trade-in, and potential mobility have made mobile homes extremely popular. Annual shipments of this type of home have increased from 1300 in 1930, to 60,000 in 1947, 119,000 in 1957, 240,000 in 1967, and to over 400,000 in 1970, according to the MHMA. Mobile homes are especially attractive to those at the ends of the age scale. About 40% of mobile home owners are below 34 years of age, 25% are above 55; 2.7 persons per home is average. Fully 50% have incomes of under $6,000 per year.

Increased sophistication in the design and construction of mobile homes has opened up a number of new markets. Traditional uses such as vacation houses, construction offices, and emergency housing have been supplemented by cores for finished houses, warehouses, schools, mobile libraries, and clinics. Many exhibition spaces (and more recently, even theatres) depend primarily on their mobility. Others, like the sectionalized house and the combination of sectional units into rows and two story units and more complex arrangements, have developed out of the inherent advantages of this sort of production.

An enormous potential market exists in the possibility of combining finished units into row houses and low and high-rise housing as soon as problems of structure, fire-resistance, sound isolation, spatial organization, and circulation are overcome. Some of the most interesting projects of the "Operation Breakthrough" program attack this problem.

THE SECTIONALIZED HOUSE   As mobile home units become increasingly immobile, and as the economies of mobile home construction are applied to larger, more complex, and expensive houses in a wider market, many prefabricators are turning to the sectional house.

The sectional house, though it began with the idea of simply combining mobile home units, has developed into a more flexible system of large-scale components. Today, sectional houses have begun to look more like conventional houses than mobile homes. The flat roof, so often identified with trailers, has been modified to various pitches. Interior and exterior materials and finishes tend to resemble those of conventional houses, as do the foundations on which they are set. Many sectional homes now meet all FHA standards.

VOLUMETRIC HOUSING SYSTEMS

Source: *Volumetric Housing Systems*, Boise Cascade.

boise cascade housing development

TOWNHOUSE

ZONES
PRIVATE: BEDROOMS BATHS
MEETING: LIVING FAMILY DINING
TRANSITION: CORRIDORS STAIRS ENTRY
SERVICE: UTILITY STORAGE MECHANICAL KITCHEN

RULES
●ENTRY AS CENTER OF CIRCULA-TION●KITCHEN···FAMILY CONNEC-TION●UTILITY···FAMILY CONNEC-TION●FORMAL MEETING SUBZONE OPPOSITE TRANSITION ZONE●

INTERNAL FLOW CHART

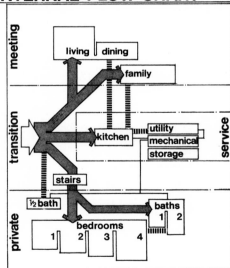

GARDEN APARTMENT

ZONES
PRIVATE: BEDROOMS BATH
MEETING: LIVING DINING
TRANSITION: CORRIDOR ENTRY
SERVICE: UTILITY STORAGE MECHANICAL KITCHEN

RULES
●ENTRY AS CENTER OF CIRCULA-TION●THRU FLOW●DUAL ORIEN-TATION●MEETING ZONE OPPOSITE EXTERIOR SERVICE ZONE●

INTERNAL FLOW CHART

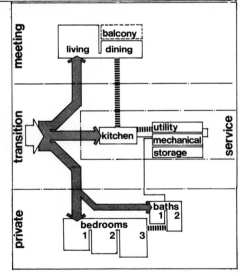

INTERIOR PLAN THEORY

By establishing a plan theory based on user needs for dwelling units in general, a design framework has been created. The internal design of the Boise Cascade housing system is based on a theory of usage "zones" and "rules." Four "zones" have been identified:

PRIVATE   Quiet, personal spaces. (bathrooms, bedrooms)

MEETING   Less quiet, communal spaces. (living, family and dining rooms)

TRANSITION   Connecting spaces (stairs, corridors, entries)

SERVICE   Support spaces (kitchens, storage rooms, mechancial spaces, utility room)

The approximate location and relationships of these "zones" are determined by "rules." Some of the "rules" which evolved during the planning study can be summarized as follows:

- Ground-level living areas should be oriented to the opposite side, since most units (townhouse or garden apartment) will have parking on the entry side of the building.

- Entries should not be directly into living spaces but should be into a circulation space from which various parts of the unit can be reached.

- Townhouse plans should allow all bedrooms to be on the second floor, and stairs to be accessible from entry space.

- Family rooms, when included, should have access to the kitchen.

- Plans should allow for the inclusion of eat-in kitchens and/or separate dining room arrangements.

- Living rooms should have the capability of expanding beyond the limits of 12' module; therefore living rooms and dining rooms should ideally be located adjacently to each other or in an "L"-shaped configuration.

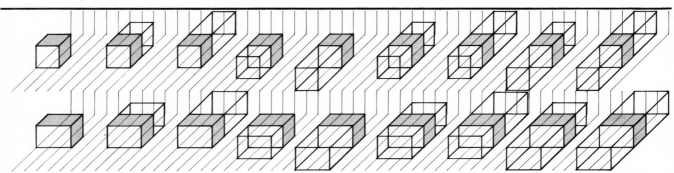

equipment (furnaces, water heaters, bathrooms, kitchens and laundries). Dry cores are made up of vertical and horizontal circulation (primary carpentry - doors, stairs, closets and halls). Each Boise Cascade module can contain either a wet or dry core in which the complex elements of that module are concentrated and standardized. The remainder of the module is filled out with the simpler living spaces such as bedrooms, living rooms and family rooms.

To allow for wide plan variations — these spaces can be adjusted in size and shape or eliminated completely during production.

A module width of twelve feet is the maximum uniformly permitted in all states for over-the-road shipments. Length and height are set by transporter design and road rules at about 55′ and 11′ respectively.

DIMENSIONAL FLEXIBILITY

Dimensional ranges within these parameters, however, are quite flexibile. Investigation indicated that modules of 10′ and 12′ in width, and 20′ to 42′ in length provided an extensive array of floor plans as will be illustrated further in the Module Array on the following pages.

MODULE COMBINATIONS

CORE-BASED DESIGN

DRY MODULE		WET MODULE

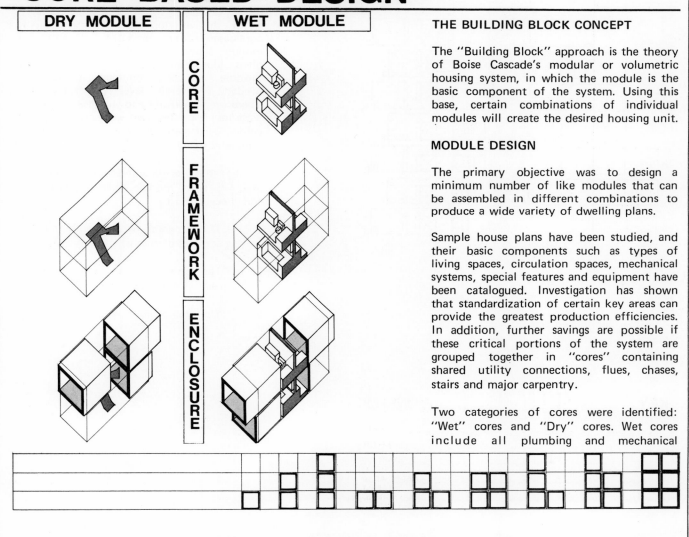

C
O
R
E

F
R
A
M
E
W
O
R
K

E
N
C
L
O
S
U
R
E

THE BUILDING BLOCK CONCEPT

The "Building Block" approach is the theory of Boise Cascade's modular or volumetric housing system, in which the module is the basic component of the system. Using this base, certain combinations of individual modules will create the desired housing unit.

MODULE DESIGN

The primary objective was to design a minimum number of like modules that can be assembled in different combinations to produce a wide variety of dwelling plans.

Sample house plans have been studied, and their basic components such as types of living spaces, circulation spaces, mechanical systems, special features and equipment have been catalogued. Investigation has shown that standardization of certain key areas can provide the greatest production efficiencies. In addition, further savings are possible if these critical portions of the system are grouped together in "cores" containing shared utility connections, flues, chases, stairs and major carpentry.

Two categories of cores were identified: "Wet" cores and "Dry" cores. Wet cores include all plumbing and mechanical

APARTMENT

DRY **WET**

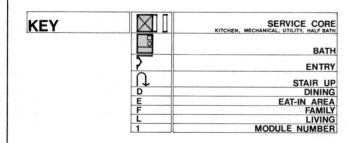

MODULE ARRAY

From the interior plan theory and the core-based design concept an array of module types has been developed. In the plans illustrated, one wet and one dry module are the minimum components needed for each level of living unit. Therefore, a two-story townhouse requires at least four modules, two wet and two dry. A garden apartment on one level requires a minimum of one each.

In the array, a fixed element, or core, is used in each module. Living spaces are added according to:

1.   The program requirements (number and size of rooms).

2.   The interior plan theory (room relationships and locations).

3.   The type of core (wet, dry).

KEY		
	⊠▯	SERVICE CORE KITCHEN, MECHANICAL, UTILITY, HALF BATH
		BATH
		ENTRY
		STAIR UP
D		DINING
E		EAT-IN AREA
F		FAMILY
L		LIVING
1		MODULE NUMBER

TOWNHOUSE

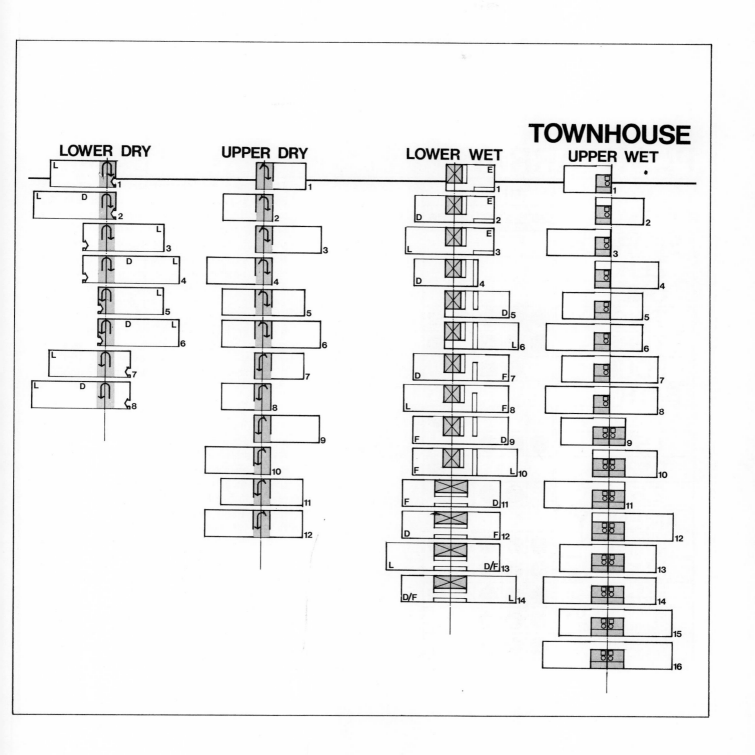

LOWER DRY

UPPER DRY

LOWER WET

UPPER WET

PLAN ARRAY

	TH 20'	TH 22'	TH 24'	GA 24'	GA 36'
BEDROOM					
ZERO				●	
ONE				●	
TWO	●	●	●	●	●
THREE	●	●	●		●
FOUR		●	●		
BATH					
1				●	●
1.5	●	●	●		
2				●	●
2.5		●	●		
AMENITY					
LIVE, EAT-IN KITCHEN	●	●	●	●	
LIVE-DINE COMBINATION	●	●	●		
LIVE, DINE DISTINCT	●	●	●		●
LIVE-DINE OR FAMILY-DINE	●	●	●		
LIVE, DINE, FAMILY DISTINCT	●	●	●		

The chart at left reflects the range of building types and widths which can be created by combinations of modules selected from the array to meet various programmatic requirements. It can be seen that for every plan type (townhouse and garden apartment) a variety of unit widths, room counts and interior amenities are available. In addition, a range of unit sizes in square feet can be obtained for many of the plan configurations. Using only the basic module designs in the module array in different combinations, over 150 distinct plans have been assembled for townhouses alone.

As examples of the kinds of plans which can be included in the plan array, and to show how the basic modules are combined, hypothetical programs were used to generate the plans at right. These plans illustrate the planning flexibility which is possible within the building system. Within the "Building Block" concept are plans having several alternatives for floor plans including separate living, dining and family rooms and a variety of combinations for these rooms. Also available are other bedroom counts and bathrooms arrangements. These plans reflect only one way of assembling the plan types shown. Other module combinations may be used to obtain a range of square foot sizes or to change the relative room sizes or unit width for a specific site application.

MODULE APPLICATION

TOWNHOUSES
4 BEDROOM, 2 ½ BATH

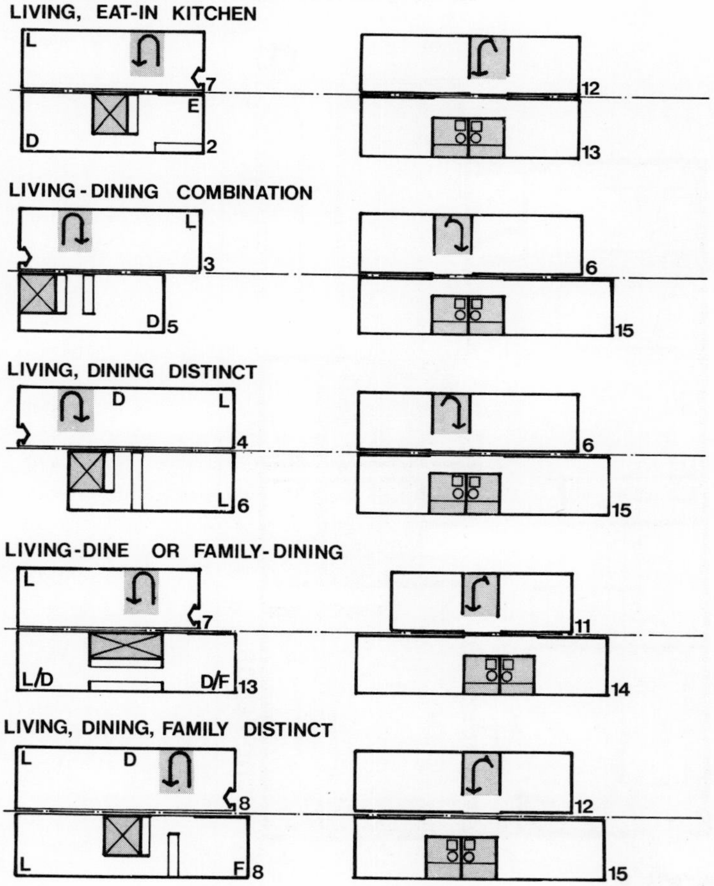

LIVING, EAT-IN KITCHEN

LIVING - DINING COMBINATION

LIVING, DINING DISTINCT

LIVING-DINE OR FAMILY-DINING

LIVING, DINING, FAMILY DISTINCT

APARTMENTS
2 BEDROOM, 1 BATH

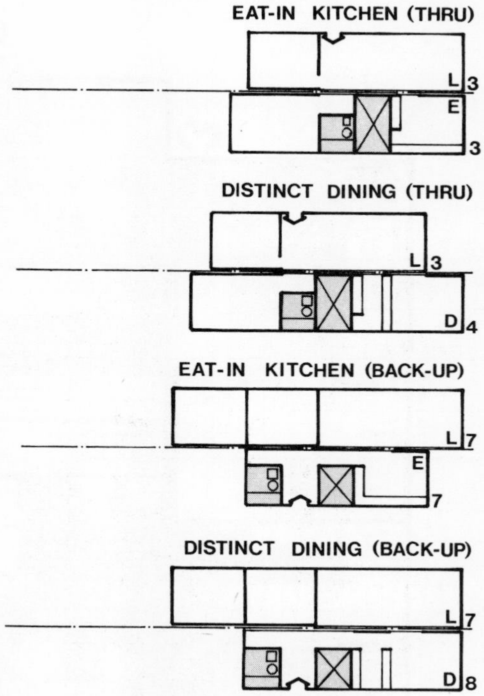

EAT-IN KITCHEN (THRU)

DISTINCT DINING (THRU)

EAT-IN KITCHEN (BACK-UP)

DISTINCT DINING (BACK-UP)

TOWNHOUSE

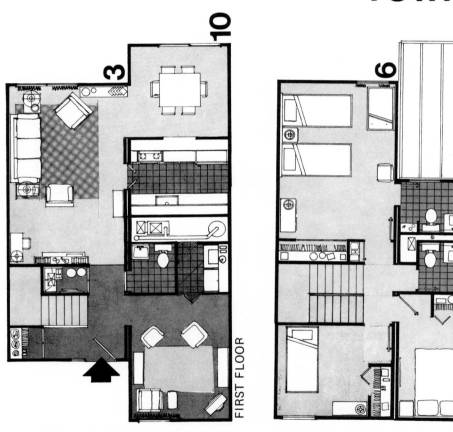

FIRST FLOOR

SECOND FLOOR

3 BEDROOM, 2.5 BATH

PLAN APPLICATION

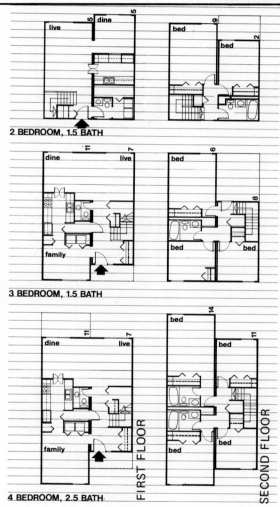

2 BEDROOM, 1.5 BATH

3 BEDROOM, 1.5 BATH

4 BEDROOM, 2.5 BATH

FIRST FLOOR

SECOND FLOOR

Through the Department of Housing and Urban Development's Operation Breakthrough Program, Boise Cascade Housing Development plans to produce units for sites in Macon, Georgia, Memphis, Tennessee, and Sacramento, Calif. A total of 244 dwelling units will be provided, ranging from 696 square feet to 1536 square feet.

Using the building programs specified by the prototype site developer on each site, plans were selected from the plan array which most nearly satisfied the development program and local housing requirements. These plans reflect space planning rules established by HUD's Operation Breakthrough guide criteria, which specify the use of space rather than abstract size requirements. Use of the criteria has allowed somewhat more space planning flexibility, yet final design plans appear to be compatible with most FHA and Model Code Standards. Plans scheduled to be produced under Operation Breakthrough are:

TOWNHOUSES

2 bedroom	1036 sq.ft.
3 Bedroom, 1.5 baths	1248 sq.ft.
3 Bedroom, 2.5 baths	1348 sq.ft.
4 Bedroom	1536 sq.ft.

GARDEN APARTMENTS

Six different plans are being used, three of which are shown:

1 Bedroom, eat-in kitchen	696 sq. ft.
	(not shown)
1 Bedroom, dining room	744 sq. ft.
2 Bedroom, eat-in-kitchen	864 sq. ft.
	(not shown)
2 Bedroom, dining room	912 sq. ft.
2 Bedroom, 2 baths	1008 sq. ft.
	(not shown)
3 Bedrooms	1128 sq. ft.

GARDEN APARTMENT ▶

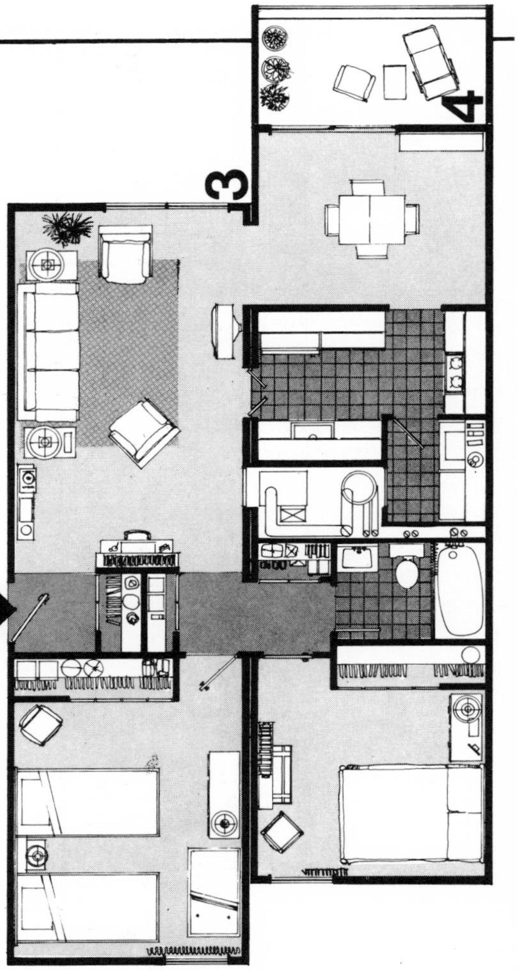

1 BEDROOM, 1 BATH   3 BEDROOM, 2 BATH

2 BEDROOM, 1 BATH

Shipping problems still limit the size and weight of each unit. Highway regulations often confine units to ten or twelve feet in width, thirteen and one-half feet in height, and about sixty feet in length. But gradual relaxation of these rules (14 feet in some western states, wider widths in "convoy") and the combination of two or more sections makes possible varied and comfortable plans which do not require the complications of fold-outs, extensions, and telescoping sections.

Local code problems are being reduced as the states adopt Factory-Built Housing laws and as units become larger and begin to look more like houses than trailers. New methods of placing and positioning units on foundations have eliminated the need for costly cranes. Greater plan flexibility is becoming possible as related sections are developed. Excellent designers are being drawn to the field as the market grows. As problems are eliminated, the sectionalized house begins to look like the prefabricator's best approach to the lower-cost house market.

A great deal can be learned from the success of the factory finished house industry. It has made the industrial production of houses a reality.

Wooden sectional unit being lifted into place. (Photo courtesy of Tom Mitchell, Jr.)

Housing unit by Stressed Structures being lifted into place.

The factors behind this success are:

1. The population is becoming increasingly mobile. Activities and people are shifting and there is something of the new popular plug-in, clip-on, throw-away, paper cup culture in sectional homes.

2. There is a framework. The industry sees itself as an industry. The manufacturers' associations and trade publications are important arenas in which standards are set. Research is undertaken and information exchanged. There is a framework for industry involvement in the legal and regulatory aspects of building.

3. The market has been organized. A structure of dealerships, sales, and service organizations and communities has been formed. The mobile home industry's involvement in an improvement of the mobile home "park" has produced the kind of setting home owners now demand.

4. Production methods are in scale with both the product and the market. Enough volume is brought to the plant to take advantage of tools, jigs, large-scale purchases, organizations, and specialization of the work. Materials are worked by special equipment, but this equipment is flexible enough to make the small production runs which allow for plan flexibility. The process is tailored to the products.

5. Financing is not cumbersome. It is closer to appliance and automobile financing than that of traditional houses.

6. The use of these techniques leads to the production of living units which compete successfully in cost and quality with other current production methods.

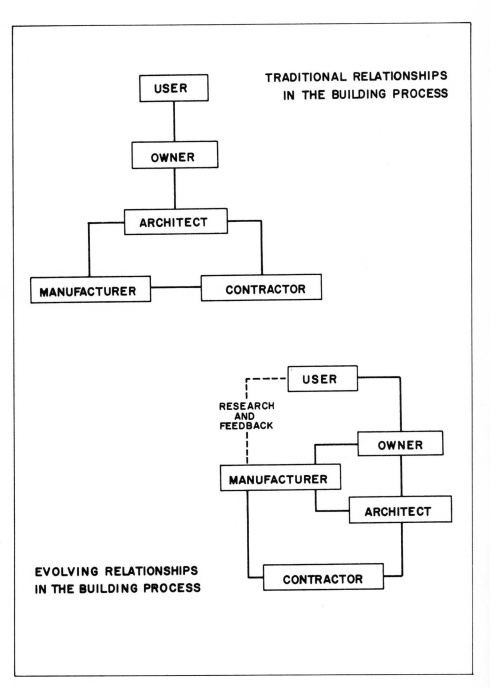

TRADITIONAL RELATIONSHIPS
IN THE BUILDING PROCESS

USER

OWNER

ARCHITECT

MANUFACTURER

CONTRACTOR

RESEARCH
AND
FEEDBACK

USER

OWNER

MANUFACTURER

ARCHITECT

CONTRACTOR

EVOLVING RELATIONSHIPS
IN THE BUILDING PROCESS

the contents of the miscellaneous file II: the structure of the industry

This review of the state of the technologies of materials and methods in building makes it clear that this area of the industry has been changing within a context of general industrial change. These changes have been accompanied by significant rearrangements in the organization of the building industry.

1. Building as an assembly operation

Building is rapidly becoming the responsibility of a new kind of construction organization. As building changes from its craft-orientation to become an assembly operation, the nature of its organization also changes. The traditional general contractors, oriented toward one of the major crafts, began to give way to large-scale building organizations undertaking enormous public projects in the aftermath of the Depression and World War II. The scale of these projects induced many entrepreneurs to approach building in the manner of the great manufacturing industries. A host of new management and production techniques were intro-duced to manage building as a manufacturing process. Time and motion studies, cost analysis, prefabrication, on-site factory production, and job analysis are, today, a part of the building industry. But these are beyond the capabilities of the small, home-based building contractor.

In many cases, the builder has taken a hand in the development of those products and materials he requires. In other cases, the manufacturer has had to come onto the building site to be effective. Package builders, precut package suppliers, precasting and system building do not fit conventional categories. The builder must constantly revise his concept of his sphere. His employees must find new occupational identities.

2. The changing role of the manufacturer

As the manufacturer's product becomes more related to building and to specific buildings, he is drawn into a new job relation. The producer of a structure-ceiling system for a school stands in a much closer relationship to the building process than does the manufacturer of roof deck and rolled shapes. Similarly, the manufacturer of aluminum door frames, plastic gaskets, or precast wall panels will be more intimately involved in specific buildings than was the manufacturer of bar stock, bulk plastics, or ready-mix concrete.

When the manufacturer stops selling his product to a subcontractor, who works with a general contractor, whose specifications are in turn made by an architect. and begins to deal directly with the owner, or with the owner and his architect, the roles of all the participants in the process are changed. Feedback from the user has an increased affect on the product. Similarly, the manufacturer's continuing involvement in the building, via maintenance, repairs, parts replacement, or trade-in for new products developed, will also change the accepted roles of architect, builder, manufacturer, and user.

3. The development of new markets

New technology for building has been made possible by significant changes in the market. These market changes have taken several forms: increasing population; the shift of populations from rural to urban locations; and the acceleration of obsolescence account for a major increase in the volume of construction.

New ways to organize the market have been devised. The housing development, local planning and state housing authorities, and the U.S. Department of Housing and Urban Development have formed large numbers of individual users into new markets. Many institutions use the leverage of their position, status, or purchasing power to enter the market. For example, we find labor unions building housing, churches, department stores, restaurant chains, and hotels. Large building programs have become major forces in the market. Cooperatives and condominiums have brought changes to residential building, as has the dealer in mobile homes.

The organization of a special market by the user has offered many new possibilities. SCSD and some of the systems development projects which followed it are good examples of this approach as is the Federal Government's awareness of itself as a major purchaser of housing, office buildings, hospitals, and post offices.

New institutions, such as the State University Construction Fund and the Urban Development Corporation in New York, are useful in setting standards, improving quality, and lowering the costs of large building programs. Government programs, ranging from "Title One," to "Turnkey Housing," and "Rent Subsidies," influence location and scheduling of construction, quality, and the relation between construction costs and rent.

New concepts of the market are significant. The city or the community is seen as a product. Whole new towns are built and the concept of a "shelter industry" concerned with the creation of environments rather than individual buildings creates a broad view of the market. Emphasis shifts to the user rather than the client. The real client is the tenant, not the Housing Authority; the school is used by the student and teacher, not the Board of Education. This has tended to move the market toward a performance oriented building. In addition, ideas such as the "unfinished but habitable house," "do-it-yourself" and "self-help" housing, are attractive to large numbers of people. They promise to form the basis for new directions in the building industry.

Continued thought has been given to methods of aggregating markets. This is a basic requirement of the new, highly capitalized building participants. Unless a market promises to make full use of capitalized facilities, industry will hesitate to invest in the field.

The traditional image of aid to industry includes direct subsidy, depreciation allowances, and tax abatement. But some of the most effective aids to building have involved help for the consumer rather than the producer. FHA mortgage insurance, loans and grants for sewer and water works, and investment in improved transportation have helped to convert need to demand by making the basis for suburban development. A market was aggregated for the early steps toward industrialization by the entrepreneurs of apartment houses and housing projects as well as the tract builder. Pensions, social security, the "G.I. Bill," and more recently rent subsidies have had the indirect effect of aggregating a market by putting resources in the hands of the buyer. Recent plans to provide a guaranteed minimal annual wage for every American can put the resources for improved housing into the hands of low-income families.

4. The necessity for new standards

The proliferation of new materials and products, the emergence of new users for old products, new uses for buildings, a new scale of buildings and building groups—all call for a new system of standards.

Traditional approaches such as adoption of modular dimensioning, compatible joining systems, and material specification have only a limited applicability to today's building problems. Setting of standards at the local or regional level, on the basis of product specification, imposes limits on innovation and constrains those aspects of building which require centralized manufacturing for a national or world market.

Manufacturers cannot mass-produce commodities or components unless they are assured of code acceptance throughout their market. New products cannot be bid fairly against old ones until standards are based on performance rather than the specification of traditional materials and configurations. Parts interchangeability, ease of assembly, maintenance, and replacement are basic requirements of modern industry and depend on meaningful standards. The same is true of insurance, sales, and the financing of buildings.

The large markets which generate the volume necessary to reduce the unit price of industrial overhead are dependent on dimensional and joint compatibility, interchange-ability, quality control, and code acceptance.

Two innovations which would be of great help in creating these markets are: (1) The use of performance as the basis for standards and codes and (2) the establishment of a national system for certification and acceptance of building products.

THE PERFORMANCE APPROACH

The performance approach is an attempt to measure the ability of a building material, component, or system to fulfill specified requirements of a user. This performance should be measured, without regard to the materials, the design, or the construction methods used by tests which simulate actual service. In practice, this process falls into four stages:

1. The performance approach begins with an analysis of the needs of a user—*performance requirements*. These requirements can be stated in narrative form, and they may be expressed before potential solutions or test techniques are created.

2. *Performance criteria* indicate, by some measurable technique, how well a product meets performance requirements. Design must provide technical solutions, and research must test methods before performance criteria can be used.

3. *Performance specifications* are created by setting acceptable limits to the performance criteria as measured by given tests. These limits are based on standards of performance developed out of common use or set by a recognized industry organization.

4. A *performance code* is a body of performance standards and specifications adopted and put into use in a legal sense.

As the product changes from raw materials of fixed chemical and physical properties to finished components, the necessity for standards based on performance becomes clear. Efforts are being made to shift to a performance basis in building codes, insurance programs, financial standards, and architectural specifications. The SCSD, URBS, ABS, PBS—Office Building Project and a number of other systems projects have used performance specifications with the expectation that a clear description of requirements and a guaranteed market will prompt development of new products or aid in the selection of existing ones.

ACCEPTANCE   Acceptance means an assessment by a recognized agency and the certification of the suitability of materials, components, or systems for a given purpose in building.

Many European countries have systems for introducing innovation into building construction. The French "Service de L'Agrément," established in 1945, is perhaps the most influential. It has led to the development of "L'Union Européene pour l'Agrément technique dans la construction," an organization formed "to ensure the equal validity of acceptance seals delivered by its members in their various countries." It was formed to aid in the development of new building materials and methods which were designed to solve problems arising out of material and labor shortages in the wake of World War II.

Acceptance (l'agrément) is a certification given to products that: (1) are on the market; (2) can be identified; (3) have a given purpose or use.

Acceptance is meant to relieve the user of the need to carry out individual investigations into the suitability of new building materials and methods. It does this by organizing a testing and reporting service designed to provide the industry with the best advice available in light of the present-day knowledge of the most informed specialists.

In practice, acceptance is only a favorable technical assessment. It has no administrative value in itself, and is neither an authorization nor a guarantee. But public authorities, insurance companies, trade associations, architects, and owners may state that they will accept new products if, or only if, they have received the acceptance seal. In the United States, there are isolated cerification procedures such as the approval of the Underwriters Laboratory for electrical work, which are used in this way, but the lack of a system to certify new building products puts an enormous burden on both the producer and the user. This lack, a significant roadblock to innovation, is being attacked in legislation now before the Congress of the United States. Separate bills propose the formation of a federal agency which could undertake testing and certification of new products and which apply federal standards to factory-made housing.

With materials and methods of increasing complexity, the advantages of the use of a performance approach in the acceptance procedure becomes clear. Certification on the basis of "How does it perform?" is of far greater value than one on the basis "Of what is it made?".

HUD's difficulties in establishing acceptance performance specifications for Operation Breakthrough and the difficulty in finding institutions capable of performing the required tests demonstrate the great need for work in this area. We are a long way from being able to make statements about needs and the performance required to meet them. New criteria, test centers, and tests as well as an entirely new institutional structure are necessary before the manufacturer of building components can be moved into the mainstream of American industry.

One of the most significant of these changes will involve the redefinition of house and furniture, of public and private, real estate and personal property, and the introduction of standards controlling quality and of institutions protecting the consumer. This clearly calls for major efforts in research and general system design.

5. The need for research

Judged by the standards of the industrial community, building is far behind in the allocation of funds for research. Clear statistics are not available for the same reasons that there is a lack of research: the industry is fragmented; it lacks an image of itself as an industry. The few large organizations which are building-oriented are small by industrial standards. The largest organizations are material-oriented; and the industry has a traditional product, rather than performance, orientation. Since there is no large framework to invite a pooling of effort which would organize and distribute the available information, and point a direction, the research of manufacturers, users, governments, trade associations, and universities is generally scattered and disorganized.

Outside of building, industry's approach to research has been quite different. Most successful companies assemble groups of capable, specially trained men and concentrate them on scientifically planned experimentation. They provide special equipment and construct facilities to ensure that these men will work effectively. They reorganize their operations to place research and development on the same basis as industry's three other principal activities: production, sales, and finance. This activity is integrated into commercial operations, coordinated with the company's other activities, and is given the opportunity to influence the company's operation policy.

New techniques have been developed for accepting innovations. It is understood that it is easier to invent something than to get it produced and used on a commercial scale. Developed procedures of these companies link the scientists and the laboratory with those people who have an intimate knowledge of user needs, and the demand of the market.

Since building has not been thought of as an area for research, very little financing has been available. As a result, there are few trained researchers and the schools, to date, have not trained many more. One of the most important challenges to the industry will be the organization and aggregation of support for research.

A great step toward the expansion of meaningful research activity was taken with the organization of The Institute for Applied Technology in the National Bureau of Standards. This institution has demonstrated an ability to undertake valuable work in research and in the definition of performance standards, which can serve as the cornerstone of an acceptance system. Research is an increasingly more important aspect of architectural education. More building research than ever before is being carried out in universities and foundations, and programs to train researchers have been inaugurated.

The establishment of the U. S. Department of Housing and Urban Development was another major step forward, but the fact that Robert Wood, after three years as Under-Secretary of this Department, could say that he had more research money available in his previous job, as head of the Political Science Department at M.I.T., indicates that change comes slowly in this area.

The research capacity of HUD is steadily growing. In 1969 Harold Finger became the first Assistant Secretary for Urban Research and Technology. The department's efforts have moved from small scale projects like the Low Income Housing Demonstrations and tentative efforts like the In-cities Research and Development Project to major undertakings such as Operation Breakthrough.

It may be years before "Breakthrough" can be fully evaluated; however, its success seems clear. HUD's efforts in this project have captured the imagination of industry, caused an enormous amount of accelerated activity, focused attention on the development of codes, testing, and education, and, in general, have given manufacturers the sense of an industrialized building industry in the United States.

This program will bring the vague outline of a building industry into focus. This is a vital prerequisite for the understanding of alternative goals, tools, and institutions.

OPERATION BREAKTHROUGH   The problem of building research presents the familiar "chicken-egg" dilemma. Which comes first, the investment or the market?

The market for industrialized building will not exist until production and its supporting network reaches the volume at which unit prices are low. On the other hand, there is no market to justify new investment until the price is low; economy is not possible without volume, volume is impossible without economy.

Capital will not take the risk to build a new industry in advance of a market. At the same time, individual market aggregation schemes have been able to guarantee a one-time market, but not the continuity in time which investors demand.

With the idea of encouraging the development of a group of building systems similar to those proving successful in Europe, the Congress of the United States added Section S-108 to the Housing Law of 1968. With requirements of concrete panel systems in mind, the law authorized a program which could guarantee a market of 1000 units a year for five years, for each of five systems. The idea is clear. A guaranteed market will stimulate investment in factories. Factories, once built, can compete on the basis of lower price. Before this program could be implemented, a new administration took office in Washington. The new secretary of HUD, George Romney, decided to make a much broader commitment to this strategy: Operation Breakthrough was launched.

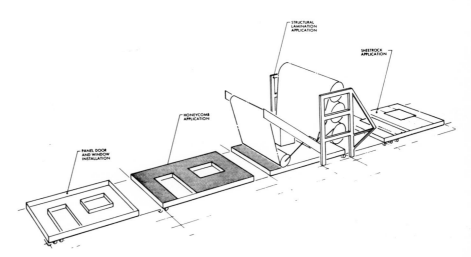

This system developed by TRW, known for their work in aerospace and transportation systems, proposes a production line to manufacture honey-comb panels. These would be fire protected by sheetrock and reinforced and finished by plastic. The panels are preassembled into volumetric modules which are transported to the site. These units are part of the Breakthrough site in Sacramento, California. Building Systems Development Inc. were consultants.

(Right) Levitt Technology Corporation's Breakthrough proposal suggests the use of "clip-ons" to modify their factory made house modules. Levitt Homes on the Kalamazoo site were among the first completed in the Breakthrough program.

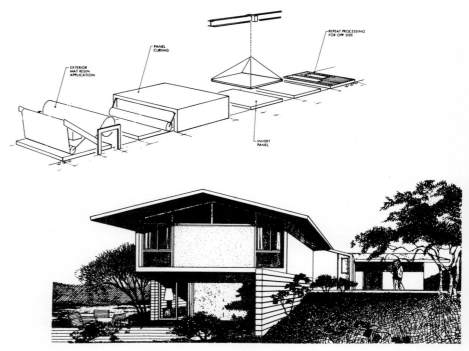

TRW systems.

(Right) Breakthrough proposal by Building Systems International, Inc. This system employs the Balency System, which is one of the more successful European systems, to answer the criteria of Operation Breakthrough. This system is already operational in the U.S.

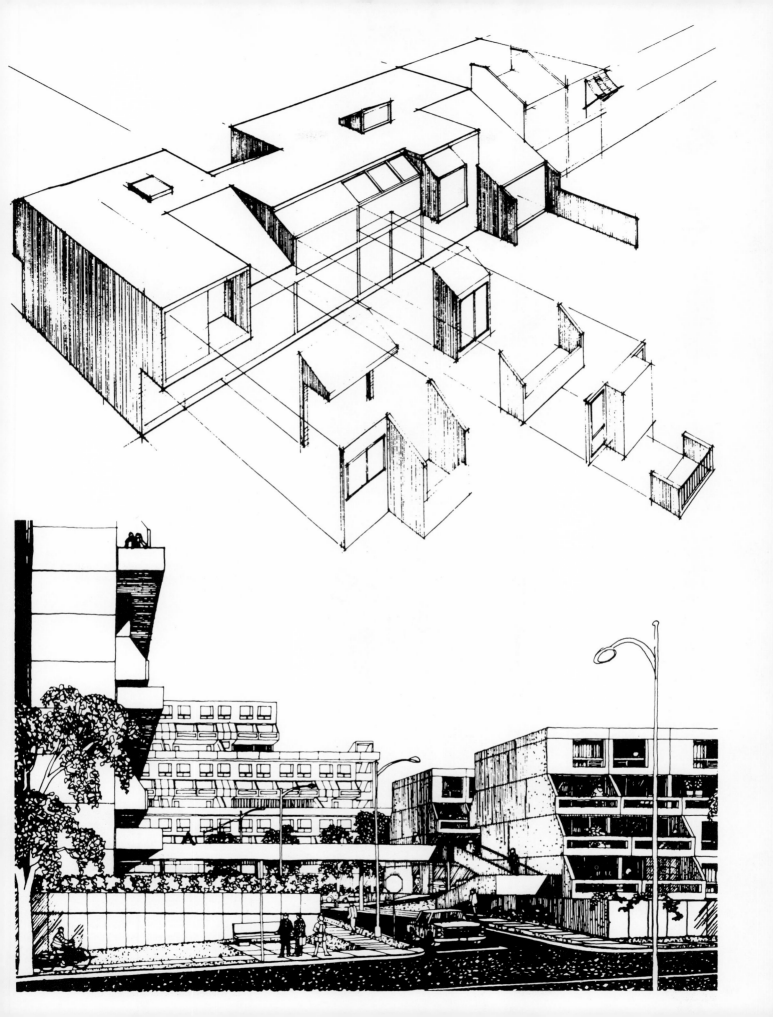

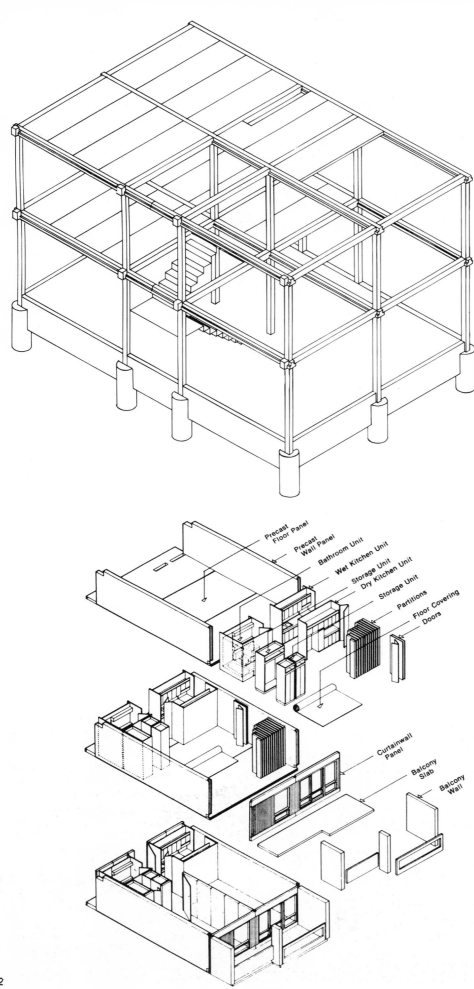

(Left) Midcity-Mitchell: Neil Mitchell's system has been successfully used to provide low-cost housing in the U.S. and abroad. It uses simple techniques to form a highly flexible skeleton for housing.

(Right) Diagram of the Factory Built House Core proposed by National Homes for Operation Breakthrough.

(Left) How a precoordinated "kit of parts" can be assembled into a room or dwelling size unit is shown by Descon/Concordia.

Precast Floor Panel
Precast Wall Panel
Bathroom Unit
Wet Kitchen Unit
Storage Unit
Dry Kitchen Unit
Storage Unit
Partitions
Floor Covering
Doors

Curtainwall Panel
Balcony Slab
Balcony Wall

(Right) National Homes' Breakthrough submission shows architectural possibilities as well as institutional and organizational problems. Natonal Homes took a more conventional approach to the actual Breakthrough buildings.

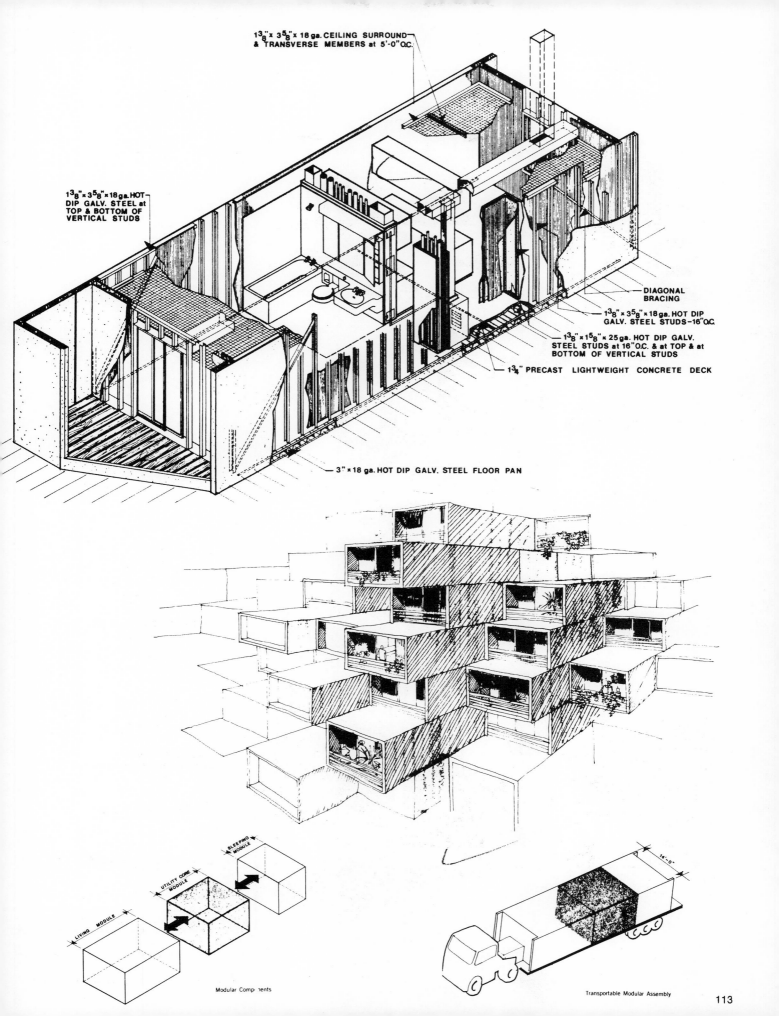

1³⁄₈" x 3⁵⁄₈" x 18 ga. CEILING SURROUND
& TRANSVERSE MEMBERS at 5'-0" O.C.

1³⁄₈" x 3⁵⁄₈" x 18 ga. HOT
DIP GALV. STEEL at
TOP & BOTTOM OF
VERTICAL STUDS

DIAGONAL
BRACING

1³⁄₈" x 3⁵⁄₈" x 18 ga. HOT DIP
GALV. STEEL STUDS-16" O.C.

1³⁄₈" x 1⁵⁄₈" x 25 ga. HOT DIP GALV.
STEEL STUDS at 16" O.C. & at TOP & at
BOTTOM OF VERTICAL STUDS

1³⁄₄" PRECAST LIGHTWEIGHT CONCRETE DECK

3" x 18 ga. HOT DIP GALV. STEEL FLOOR PAN

LIVING MODULE

UTILITY CORE MODULE

SLEEPING MODULE

14'-0"

Modular Components

Transportable Modular Assembly

113

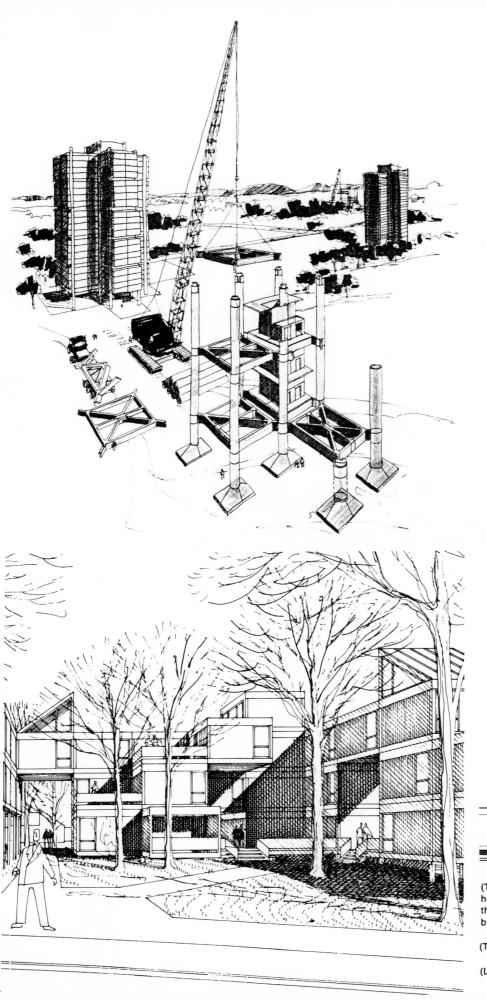

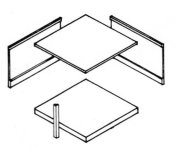

**Factory fabrication
of panels, components**

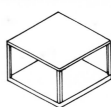

**Basic module assembly
in assembly plant**

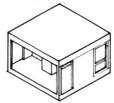

**Additional walls
and built-in equipment**

Transportation to site

(Top, left) A scheme to make factory-built
houses usable in high-rise construction
through the use of a large support structure,
by National Homes for Operation Breakthrough.

(Top, right) Breakthrough proposal by Pempton.

(Left) Breakthrough proposal by Pempton.

Operation Breakthrough was designed to use all the resources and the leverage of the Federal Government to solve the chicken-egg dilemma. A competition would identify the most promising approaches to industrialized building. The winners would be subsidized to develop (phase 1) and build (phase 2) model units on a series of selected sites around the country. The sites themselves would serve as the basis for experiments in design, construction management, and production. The finished projects would serve as "Housing Fairs" to demonstrate the new ideas and as models for regional "Brokers." Some would be lived in, some kept as models, and others exhaustively tested. They would serve as the basis for (phase 3) volume production.

Pempton, one of the Operation Breakthrough winners, is an excellent example of the "precoordinated kit of parts" system. The diagrams show how parts are coordinated into components, components into subassemblies, and subassemblies into the final building.

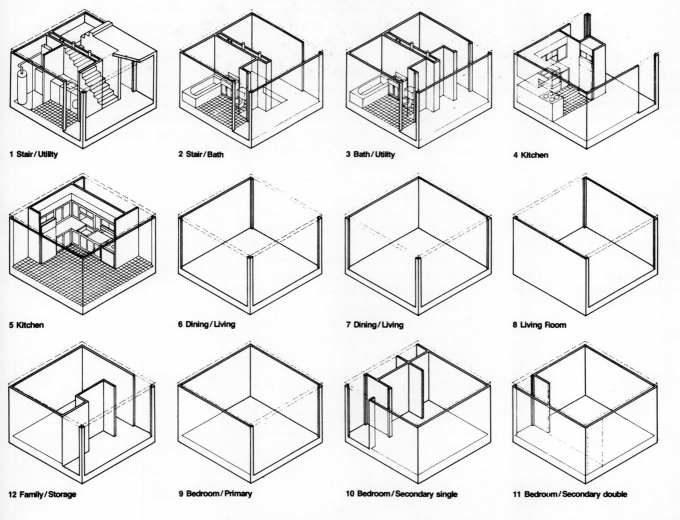

1 Stair/Utility

2 Stair/Bath

3 Bath/Utility

4 Kitchen

5 Kitchen

6 Dining/Living

7 Dining/Living

8 Living Room

12 Family/Storage

9 Bedroom/Primary

10 Bedroom/Secondary single

11 Bedroom/Secondary double

At the same time massive energy was to be expended to organize a market aggregation program throughout the United States. All of the resources of HUD, which could be diverted, would be used: sewer and water grants, mortgage insurance, and housing subsidy programs. Codes would be redesigned and methods to speed the processing of plans developed. A program in which those prototypes judged successful would be "certified" for immediate code and financial program acceptance was planned. And, in late 1971 HUD organized a "set-aside" procedure which guaranteed producers a "special window" for obtaining approval for subsidized housing.

This is the most ambitious program yet undertaken by HUD. Thousands of organizations were represented at the first bidders meeting. There were over 200 full systems submitted for evaluation. The total of all submissions, full, partial, and market aggregation schemes, was over 600.* Most of these were made by consortiums (groups or companies). Twenty-two systems were selected, as were sites, site planners, sponsors, construction managers, and developers.

A group of experiments was planned for each site, codes prepared, plans drawn, ground broken and, despite enormous problems, Breakthrough was on its way.

*See bibliography for Housing Systems Proposals for Operation Breakthrough.

Breakthrough was a success before the first ground breaking, even though it may not actually meet any of its stated goals. The problems of organizing and managing the program have brought delays and confusion. The team assembled by HUD was largely new to government. Often they were new to construction. Secretary Romney came from the automobile industry and state government, while Harold Finger, his Assistant Secretary in charge of the Program, came from the space program.

In practice, the power of the Federal Government to overcome constraints, speed processing, divert funds, etc., was weaker than anticipated while the states and local governments were less interested than the planners had hoped. The systems selected were not particularly innovative; those that were retreated under the pressures of meeting the program milestones. The success of the program depended on buildings being built; serious innovation was not possible. While some winners, like National Homes, were already leading producers, others, like the TRW Systems Group, were seeking entry into a new field. Costs rose and budgets were cut in the economic slump of the early 1970's and the number of units to be built was reduced. In the process of long, unexpected delays the hastily assembled financial structures of the consortiums were strained. A year and a half after selection, after ground was broken at the Seattle site, the Townland Consortium collapsed. Most site experiments were canceled; little more than a solid waste handling experiment is left. The program introduced a new building code that is proving more difficult to use than expected and the ideas for an exhaustive evaluation procedure are quietly slipping away.

But Breakthrough *has* succeeded. By November 1971, the first units were occupied at Kalamazoo and other sites were well under way. But more significantly, the very commitment to the program has lent a credibility to the idea. The time has finally come for industrialized building. There is hardly a major industrial organization without an iron in the fire. Auto, aerospace, and appliance companies as well as the producers of basic building materials are involved. Experiments are underway, subsidiaries and purchasing divisions are set up, and mergers are in progress. A number of new consortiums and joint ventures were organized for entry into Breakthrough. Others have remained outside. In fact, it often seems that more progress is being made by those free of constraints, delays, and the hypnotic fascination of Operation Breakthrough. Some companies hesitated, deciding that ". . . the first Christians get the biggest lions," and entered the field only after the first group of participants had thinned out. Others found the complexities and uncertainties too intimidating and left the field.

Another interesting indicator of "the state of the art" can be found in the backgrounds of the personnel involved. One of the signs of a mature industry is the development of a high level personnel exchange between the industry and Government. This has been a familiar pattern in the military, manufacturing, and financial areas. The past few years have seen scores of these exchanges in the emerging building industry. Senior corporate leaders from the auto, appliance, aerospace, and materials industries have taken on a variety of Federal assignments in agencies related to building. Top leaders from the executive branch of Government have moved into high level positions in the emerging building industry.

Perhaps when the building industry is more familiar with the reality of research, the success of Operation Breakthrough will be clear. For research is rarely the precise, linear movement from objective to goal we envision. It is random; accident plays a big part. We find things we did not expect. New goals are uncovered and the information uncovered is useful in unexpected areas. It is the "vector sum" of a great variety of energies which brings success.

The success of Breakthrough has been the spirit it has unlocked. Industrialized building has become "an idea in good currency."

Photo courtesy of Expo Corporation.

the contents of the miscellaneous file III: bits and pieces

There are a number of other things that have entered building—clear trends which run through our miscellaneous file. One of these seems to be a definite movement in new products and processes, in institutional and organizational structure, and even buildings, toward ephemeral structures, or as Buckminster Fuller has called the phenomenon, *ephemeralization.*

EPHEMERALIZATION   In short, structures are becoming lighter and lighter. There are many examples of this phenomenon. Structural ones are easiest to describe: compare Stonehenge with an Egyptian or a Greek column, trace the development on through to moulded iron and rolled steel sections, or consider some of the more recent trussed and tensegrity structures. In some recent air-supported structures we find ourselves walking through an invisible column of air. A whole class of structures has done more with less. Structures have become lighter as their material becomes stronger, assemblies optimal, and organization more sophisticated. One can find similar patterns in comparing horsepower per pound in engines, the weight of fuel required to heat a house, or the weight of the equipment it takes to communicate: in either telephone radio, TV, or computers. As technology improves, its hardware becomes lighter. Every technology displays examples of this kind. Our survey of the changes in methods and materials shows the building industry is no exception.

CLOCKS AND CLOUDS   A second phenomenon involves "software" as well as "hardware," and runs through an entire group of tools and organizations involved in the change in building. There is a change in the structure of many things around us. It is a change from a linear-mechanical structure to one of dispersion. The physicist Carl Popper has described this as a change from "clocks to clouds." It is a shift in view which is basic to an understanding of the new forms the building industry may take.

We generally understand that a clock is a machine, hard, precise, predictable. One knows exactly where each part will be, how it will operate, and what it will be doing for the given time of its operation. Our image of most mechanisms tends to be clock-like.

There is another kind of mechanism that is effective, but less easy to visualize. Its actions are more difficult to predict. A cloud is such a mechanism: a cloud in the sky, a cloud of electrons, molecules, gnats, or smoke. A school of minnows can be considered as a cloud, as can many of the institutions of our society. As we learn more about a cloud of minnows, we find we can make many of the same kind of predictions we can about the clock. The cloud moves according to certain rules. Its motion is related to temperature, sunlight, food supply, sea current, season of the year, and a host of other things. Any fish at any time can swim into or away from the group. The mechanism is invisible, but real. It controls the operation of the cloud. At some point, when the minnow finds himself a certain distance from the center of the group, he feels threatened or frightened. For some strong reason, he returns to the group and moves as a part of its pattern. There is an invisible control system. The cloud is a machine with a more complex nature than a clock, but a machine nevertheless.

Let us see how this is related to the changing structure of the building industry. In many of our approaches to industrialized building, we have assumed that we are dealing with clocklike mechanisms at the very time that these mechanisms are changing to more cloudlike forms. There are two interesting phenomena which illustrate this, one in business and the other in politics.

Tensegrity structure by Ken Snelson. (Photo by Forrest Wilson.)

Air support structure. (Photo by Peter Britton.)

Detail of a bank building by architect Don Hisaka. (Photo by Thom Abel.)

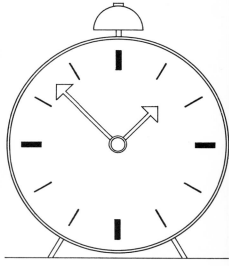

(Right) Army ants: patterns and structures, Alan Sonfist.

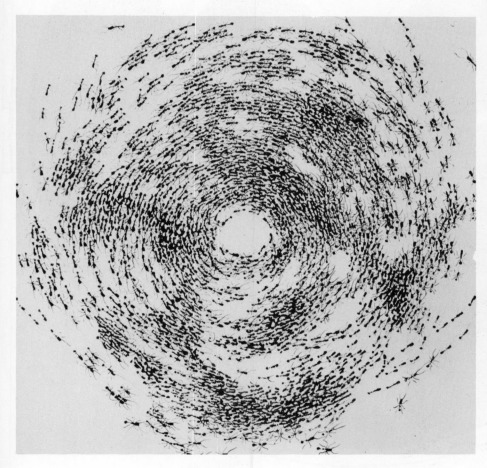

The corporation is a clocklike mechanism, it has a clear purpose, direction, and point of view. The Coca Cola Company makes soda, U. S. Steel makes steel. The structure of the corporation, its leadership, goals, and techniques have traditionally been clear. They resemble clocklike mechanisms. Yet the corporation has been restructuring itself for some time. It has become the conglomerate. There has been a steady shift from a clocklike to a cloudlike mechanism. What does Ling Temco Vaught do? What business are they in? What tools do they use? What do they make? What are their goals? Who is the leader of LTV Industries? The leaders of 19th century corporate industry were well-known figures, but the president of the giant modern corporation cannot cash a check at the supermarket without identification, any more than you or I. The control system as well as leadership, tools, and goals has become much more cloudlike, and more difficult to perceive.

Politics offers an interesting parallel. Compare the rigid structure of the Communist cell as a nineteenth century political organization with today's amorphous "Movement." People might ask the same questions of the Movement they might ask of LTV Industries. Who is the leader? What do they want? What do they do? What are their goals?

The Movement's goals go off in many different directions, and its direction is the result of many, apparently conflicting, activities. In short, it is cloudlike.

City limits.

Cloudlike mechanisms are developing all around us, in education, medicine, government, transportation, recreation, and even housing. One of the things we might look for as a basis for our new conceptual framework for building is the shift from clocklike images (a factory to make houses) to a cloudlike one. What would a cloudlike building industry look like? We will return to this analogy after we have examined all the items scattered through our miscellaneous file.

THE ESCALATION OF TECHNOLOGY

Another of these items might be called "the escalation of technology." As a technology develops, it follows a series of cycles in which each new invention solves an existing problem but creates a new problem. The new problem is on a higher level of complexity and requires a solution involving a higher technology. This poses a still larger problem, which has to be solved at a still-higher level of technology. Invention becomes the mother of necessity.

As this proceeds, escalation becomes hypnotic—eventually, solutions are seen only in terms of the technology that caused the problem. If schools are bad, we spend more money on them. If the welfare system does not work, fund a new program. If the bombing is unsuccessful, drop more bombs.

In building, there are any number of these phenomena: for example, the elevator.

The cycle begins with an increase in city land values. To lower the unit cost of land, increasingly taller buildings are built. So the elevator is invented, permitting higher buildings to be built. We take advantage of the principles of skeleton construction, and new materials, to build higher buildings. Land values increase; soon there is a need for improved elevators, since still taller buildings are demanded. Buildings get higher, the land values go up, and as land values go up, more is paid for the land. Despite problems of crowding, density, pollution, fire, noise, and congestion, it becomes impossible to think about a downtown without elevators. The solution has become part of the problem.

The computer is another good example. With it problems can be solved that could not have been considered before. However, they demand increasing complexity in the data required. One needs data to acquire data. We limit the richness of our measurements to fit the computer. Again we find that while some problems are solved, larger problems are created.

Perhaps the best example of technological spiral is seen in the development of the automobile. The original invention met a need. Therefore, a commitment was made to street construction and paving. Paved streets made cars more useful. More cars were made. Soon many people had cars, and the streets became crowded with them. Planners began their work; they reshaped the street patterns to carry the increased traffic. Wide streets, boulevards, and avenues were built. The number of cars again increased. Streets became slow, clogged, and unsafe. Freeways were invented. They cut through the city, and opened its structure. Traffic moved again. People spread out. However, the city, even in its new amorphous form, began to clog. Today the air is bad, filled with noise and smog and smells: witness the spectacle of Los Angeles. We call for a return to public transit but it is too late. In the city's new form transit lines cannot reach enough people to pay for itself. The city is now too dispersed for anything but an automobile solution.

The escalation of technology is related to another element of the miscellaneous file, which involves a relation between "ephemeralization," "clocks and clouds," and "the escalation of technology."

CYCLES OF TECHNOLOGY   As technology escalates, it moves through a series of alternating cycles from a dispersed to a specialized to a dispersed form once again.

Communications offer a good example. In a small village, everyone is able to beat a tom-tom, and anyone in the community can hear it. One does not need any special equipment or need to be hooked up to any system. If you can hear the signals, you get the message. But you can hear it only in the village. In the 19th century, we took a jump, with the invention of the telephone and telegraph. One could speak from any part of the world and be heard instantly, by anyone who is on the line. We made a trade-off between a small scale operation, dispersed and free, and a large scale operation which was linear and specialized.

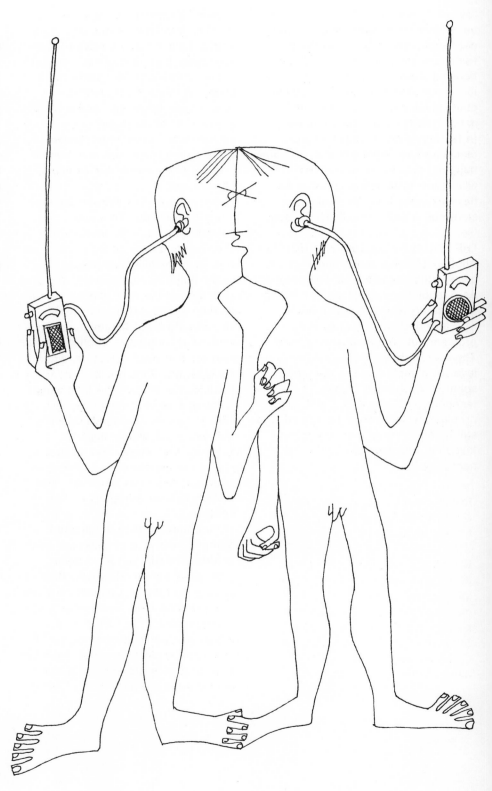

Western civilization is in the midst of that kind of specialization today. We have traded off the house that we made for ourselves or with members of our community for a house with many things that we have never had before. We have dishwashers, washing machines, and color television. But our houses are made on a take-it-or-leave-it basis. Manufacture is linear, specialized, and most often remote. We find we must take the entire system in order to enjoy a part of it. Laws reinforce this system. Most towns will not allow self-made houses, utilities will not serve them, neither will insurance companies. We are all on the line.

If we pursue this analogy, from the tom-tom to telephone to radio, television, and eventually TV interconnected with satellites, tape, cassettes, and computers, we find an interesting phenomenon. If we go far enough in this direction, we eventually emerge at the other end of the tunnel to find a new dispersed state. We move from the wire to the wireless, the track to the trackless and we no longer have to be on the line. A small piece of equipment on either end is all that is needed for the whole world to communicate.

This is the "Global Village." What once took place on the scale of a village takes place now on an international scale. If we look at building technology in this framework, we see that we have made the original jump. We are on the verge of the mastery of techniques which allow a new level of freedom.

We are moving house building from the site into the factory, but this is transitional, not an end. If we go far enough, we may finally emerge with a system in which technology begins to serve the individual instead of causing him to come to the factory to be served. This would be cloudlike rather than clocklike technology.

The "Global Village" analogy shows how we spiral from dispersed to linear to dispersed technologies of a new scale. There is an important parallel to this. Institutions as well as hardware are involved. If we look at radio as it was a generation ago, we find that a few companies were making most of the equipment needed to broadcast and receive. The same few companies also controlled the radio networks. The same organization which made it possible to use the radio controlled what the radio could say. Television takes the same form today.

It is important to understand that as technology moves from the linear to the dispersed form, as it improves past the first breakthroughs, technical developments occur which make it possible to disperse. At the same time control is removed from the hands of a few people and spread to many. As radios became cheaper and easier to make, and as the whole technology of radio broadcasting was better understood, radio was assimilated into our lives. New techniques made the radio station easier to run, cheaper and less provincial while more dispersed. The network changed from a clocklike to a cloudlike structure. There is hardly a town today that does not have several radio stations. Larger cities have many, and unlike a generation ago, when the few networks all had similar programs, they represent a wide diversity of interests and opinion.

Television today still has a small number of choices. In fact, choices are not really choices at all. But the technologies and institutions which will change this are already visible. On radio we hear talk, news, classical, rock, and country and western music; programs are devoted to weather, business, and farmer's reports as well as focused on local and national issues. We can expect, as television matures, that the same kind of change will occur; TV will become dispersed, like radio. Cable television will restructure the industry, but real change is more likely to come out of a new, more dispersed, technology—perhaps video tape cassettes. The idea that programs do not have to be listened to "on the line" or at a particular time or in a particular order or place will revolutionize the medium.

To carry this analogy a little further, the change in the technology which makes music available has done more than simply broadcast the new sounds. It has meant a much wider influence by "out-groups," by the young, by the representatives of cultures which are not part of the Establishment. Innovation comes more easily, change comes more rapidly, because music is no longer tied to established structures which shape and control the medium. Technology has moved to a point where entry into the music system is cheap and easy, and control of the tools is in the hands of many people. There has been a dispersion. A cloudlike atmosphere has replaced the clocklike mode which is still common in television.

DISCONTINUITY   The last item in the miscellaneous file involves the idea of "discontinuity." It is the most disturbing thread which runs through the material we have collected. It is disturbing because it tells us that while we plan for a future based on the continuation or acceleration of present trends, the future promises abrupt discontinuity. We really must invent a new filing system. We agree that things are changing, but we can only anticipate changes which are linear. We cannot picture a world in which things have radically changed, where there are sharp breaks or jumps—or discontinuities—between present and future.

Yet change is often discontinuous. In the development of science and technology in the thousand years before the late 18th and early 19th century, there were many inventions which were absorbed into the dispersed, medieval structure of the world. Only toward the end of the 19th century did a whole series of organizations form out of a changed view of the world. They came as part of a discontinuous jump; corporations, big cities, public utilities, and most universities were formed at that time. The bathroom, the city water system, fire and police departments, public education, and medical treatment as we understand it all emerged built on developments in the physical

sciences which had transpired in the centuries before. Since then, we have been in a relatively steady state. There have been few changes in our conceptual framework. But the last hundred years have seen great inventions and developments outside the physical sciences, in social, medical, and biological areas. We have yet to see the institutional changes which will grow out of these developments, the new institutions which will affect our lives as the building of the railroads, the steel factories, and the incorporation of the cities shaped our lives in the last century.

These are some of the trends we must begin to contemplate if we are to assemble a picture of a future building industry. They are some of the elements which our new conceptual framework must support. They are elements of an industry which will be more cloudlike just as the elements of our earlier conceptual framework made inevitable the building of the corporations and factories in clocklike form.

a shift of image

There is an optical illusion, familiar as a parlor trick, in which as one looks at the drawing of a familiar object, it suddenly changes: a vase becomes two faces. Once you see the faces, it is hard to see the vase again. Your mental set shifts, and suddenly you see things in a new and unexpected way.

We are in the midst of such a shift. Reality, organized in a fresh framework, appears in a new perspective. It becomes increasingly more difficult to see the world in traditional forms. We cannot seem to visualize a building industry other than one in which factories make houses.

Can you see what the diagrams on the right are meant to be? They are bicycle wheels, four different designs for the front wheel of a bicycle. Diagrams like these were prepared by Dr. Edward DeBono, at Cambridge University. In his book *The Mechanism of the Mind,* he describes a test. Can you predict the motion of bicycles with these front wheels? With a little mathematics and physics you can describe the motion of the bicycle with each front wheel. As DeBono points out, much of our planning for the future is based on analysis of this kind.

But when a boy "pops a wheelie," it does not make any difference what shape the front wheel of his bicycle is, he rides on the rear wheel only. In a sense, what we have been trying to do in so many of our rational analyses and plans for the future of the building industry is similar to the making of a very careful analysis of the front wheel and then "popping a wheelie." The mind assumes that the only way to ride that bicycle is on both wheels. But the minute we visualize another way of riding a bicycle, all the careful planning and logical analyses we have made do not mean very much.

Here is another example. We saw in the bicycle analogy a shift from the obvious to a variation that is just as simple and logical but unpredictable. Optical illusions present a similar phenomenon.

What do you visualize when you look at the picture to the far right? If it is a star and you look a little longer, you see cubes. Once you see the cubes, it is difficult to see the star. Once you see the star, it is hard to see the cubes.

What is interesting about the optical illusion in the context of our analysis of industrialized building is that the form changes, but none of the data has changed. All one does when viewing the star or the cubes is to put the information into a different conceptual framework. We reorganize the information into a different form based on what we are prepared to see. The data are constant. Only the image shifts. In this way, there are many things before our eyes waiting for us to see them.

Is our view of industrialized building simply one side of an optical illusion? What other views are possible? The remainder of this book will explore some alternate views.

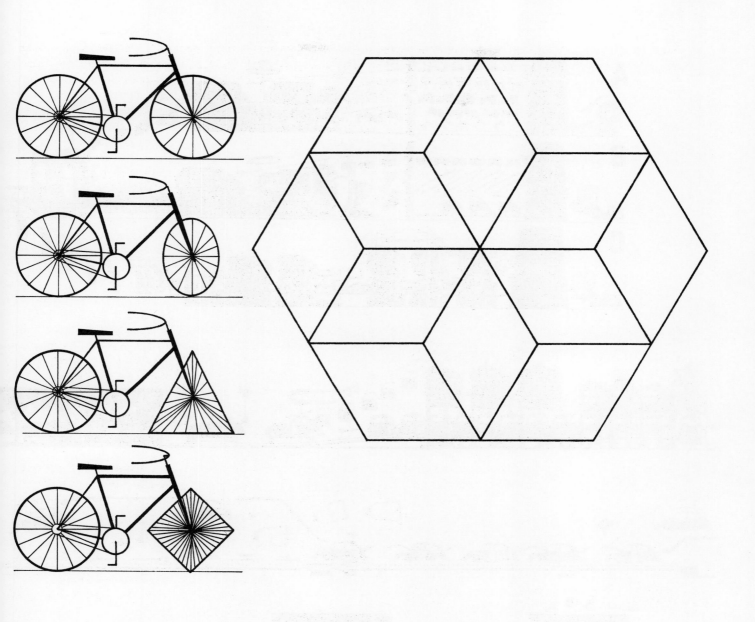

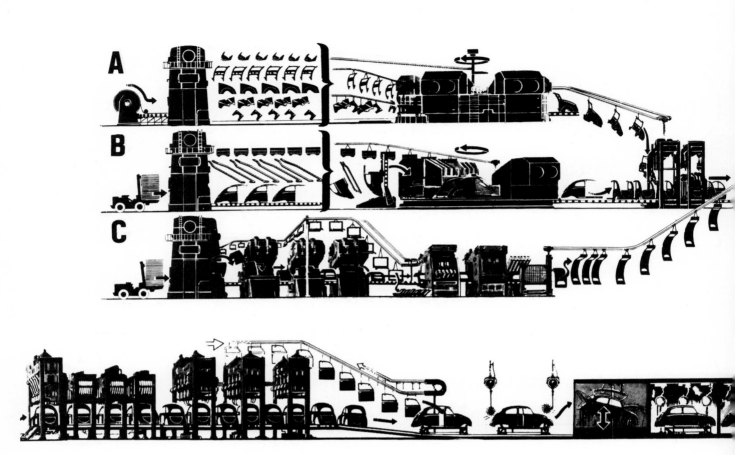

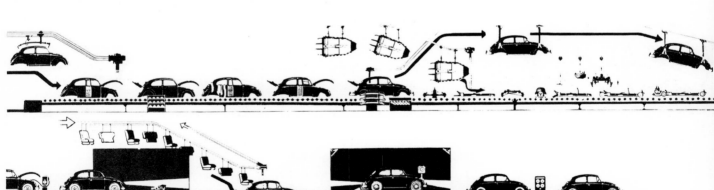

Photo courtesy of Volkswagon.

three scenarios

First Scenario: The Housing Factory

The automobile industry continues to fascinate those involved in the production of buildings. The image of houses rolling off a production line, a house a minute, seems a positive answer to the problem of housing production. The speed of production achieved in automobile factories combined with consistantly high levels of quality control are in sharp contrast to the patterns of the building industry. To comprehend the force of this contrast one has only to imagine a system in which automobiles are produced as houses are.

Picture a typical family. They have completed a year of consultation with an automobile designer. Plans have been prepared, cardboard models studied, bids have been taken, plans modified, and a builder has been selected. The plans have finally been approved by the local authorities, cost adjustments and scheduling have been completed. Construction is about to begin.

On the first day a truck arrives and dumps the first shipment of parts on the front lawn. It is raining and some of the metal parts are in danger of rusting. The contractor is at another job and does not move things under cover until the following day. A small connecting pin rolls off under a rose bush and is lost. A cardboard box containing bolts is soaked and splits open scattering small pieces around the driveway.

Once the contractor hears that the parts are at the house he sends around a crew. The family is lucky to be assigned one of the contractor's best foremen. He and his men study the plans, search out the necessary parts, and begin the work. It is an unfamiliar design and a few trial and error efforts are necessary before the frame starts to take shape. Work is held up from time to time. One of the men must go back to the shop for a tool, another calls the designer with a question. The men are idle several days waiting for a replacement for the part under the rose bush.

The pipe fitter is at his grandmother's funeral and the work is held up because the main crew cannot set the rear end until his work is done. There have been delays caused by keeping the brake system exposed until the local inspector checks it. Painting was delayed during a week of rain and the front bumper was scratched during installation with the wrong tool and has to be replaced. The rear upholstery arrived damaged. But the manufacturer discontinued his old line and the new fabric does not match the sample the family selected in the distributor's showroom.

Eventually, the car will be finished. There is a small celebration among the beer cans, sandwich ends, and parts wrappers scattered on the lawn. Six months later all of the "bugs" have been worked out. The car is running well, and the lawn looks like new. The financial details have been arranged, the construction loan paid off by a long-term bank loan, the final fees to the designer and the lawyer have been paid, and there are only a few outstanding liens and claims by subcontractors.

Compared to the process by which we actually build automobiles, this parody seems a nightmare. The cost in time and money has been enormous. Large numbers of highly paid skilled workers are inefficiently employed. Sophisticated tools are not available. There are great personal frustrations, dissatisfaction, and worry. The final product is unique and unfamiliar, built on a narrow knowledge of what is possible and what has been done by others. Automobile service stations do not stock the spare parts it requires, the mechanism for ordering them is unclear.

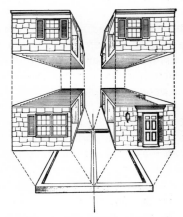

Schematic of four-part module home section of Levitt townhouse.

Townhouse built by factory assembly line methods will appear as this Levitt prototype. Units will cost $20-$25,000 each and will be initially marketed in Detroit, Chicago, Toledo and Cleveland, O.

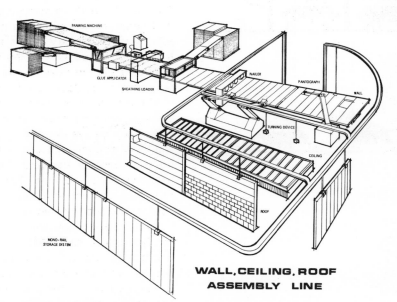

WALL, CEILING, ROOF ASSEMBLY LINE

Production line for parts of Levitt homes begins with raw materials and ends with finished components for modules. Units will be marketed to surburan areas first than to city-dwellers. Transportation costs are estimated at 75¢ to $1 per mile.

Homes to Roll Off Levitt Assembly Line

Factory-built homes will roll off a Levitt assembly line in the near future. Announcing this intention, Richard M. Wasserman, president of Levitt and Sons, Inc., said the company had formed a new subsidiary, Levitt Housing Systems Corp., to produce the homes in a plant at Battle Creek, Mich.

Charles L. Biederman has been named president of the new division. He said, "Levitt can best maintain its leadership in the home building industry by using new construction methods. Factory-built housing will enable us to draw on the semi-skilled labor pool and provide them with careers that will be profitable and secure.

"Moreover, we will maintain our ability to provide a quality home priced within the means of the moderate-income American."

The first units designed for production are townhouses upon which a 2½ year feasibility study was recently completed. Currently, studies are underway for apartments, multi-story buildings, motels, and vacation homes. The townhouses will be on permanent foundations, meet local building codes and zoning requirements and will be comparable to site-built units in structural aspects.

The Battle Creek, Mich., house factory will have a floor area of 140,000 sq. ft. The first units are expected off the assembly line in late fall, 1970, at a rate of 2,000 dwelling units per year with one work shift.

Wasserman interjected the comments that, "Sectionalized housing can be a definitive step forward in reducing the housing crisis of the 70's . . . . help solve our present shelter dilemma by providing quality housing at moderate cost."

Photo courtesy of Chevrolet Motor Company.

Photo by Del Ankers.

(Left) Photo courtesy of General Motors.

(Right) Photo courtesy Chevrolet Motor
Company.

(Left) Photo courtesy of American Plywood
Association.

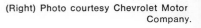

(Right) Photo courtesy of American Plywood
Association.

Many other areas can be added: the limited scale of purchasing, the transient nature of builders, difficulty of servicing, the problems involved in moving the car into other jurisdictions, finance, insurance, and taxes. The analogy can be carried much further. As we do, so bewilderment grows. Why can we not make houses as we make cars?

We are, in fact, beginning to do so. The first elements of the scenario are already visible in the factories producing mobile, sectional, and modular homes. Viewed from a distance they look like the gigantic mechanism which we have envisoned. They take raw materials and components in at one end of an assembly line and eject houses from the other.

On closer inspection we find house factories are still at an early stage of development. Both the process and the product are crude. The house produced is not significantly different from the one made on your lot. Tools and skills are only slightly changed. Nevertheless, more and more sophisticated tools are used in the factory; jigs and lifting devices are common, the work is specialized, with each worker an expert at his station. He stands indoors while the product moves past him.

Photo courtesy of Chevrolet Motor Company.

Photo courtesy of Hercoform, Inc.,
Wilmington, Del.

The product has begun to change, as has the process. Room dimensions tend to be fixed by transportation requirements rather than internal requirements. More components of the finished house are "built-in." New materials are becoming familiar as are the new methods of joining which have been made possible by modern technology. The factory can buy materials in greater quantity, in large enough volume to reduce the price and with enough market leverage to obtain special materials and dimensions. For example, factories using plywood sheets 9' × 36' can enclose an entire wall without joints. Individual builders could not handle pieces of this dimension even if they could procure them. Factory management plans production long in advance. The housing plant has storage areas and inventory and has developed a line of credit which enables them to buy in a depressed market and hold material against the demands of production.

The scenario is familiar; to develop it in more detail one has only to study the great manufacturing industries. For the same problems are posed, and the same solutions are suggested. The national context must change. Uniform building codes and finance and insurance standards must exist if the industry is to have more than a local market. Networks of dealerships and service facilities must be established to market and maintain the product. The Federal Government must take increasing responsibility to set acceptable standards, finance research and development, and to make sure people have money to buy the product. Sites must be ready to receive the product of the housing factory. To make sure these are available, Government must help provide transportation, communication, water, sewers, and power. Schools must be built along with medical facilities, shopping, and the rest of the urban infrastructure.

Financial arrangements are particularly important. A house every ten minutes is useless without a ten minute mortgage. Interim financing arrangements must be constructed to carry the cost of the product from the time it leaves the factory until it becomes real estate. In fact, the financing may prove to be a major profit item in itself. Perhaps housing can be treated as a "loss leader." Taking a broad systems view, the housing factory may decide to "give the house away" if there is enough profit in transportation, finance, installation service, and maintenance.

The housing company will do all it can to protect itself in the market. Again we can predict a series of steps. Companies will move to control the process from raw material to the maintenance of the finished product. Vertical companies can plan more effectively. At each point on the ladder the supply below is ensured as is the market above. The product can be optimized by changes across traditional boundaries. Feed-back is more direct and reliable and duplication can often be avoided. The Boise Cascade group of companies is a good example of this development. They are involved in the lumber industry, land development, building, and the management of properties.

The housing factory will lean heavily on advertising to ensure the kind of market it needs. The image of its product as a modern, stylish, inexpensive, prestigious home as well as all the other salable characteristics must be maintained. Advertising is one of the great safety mechanisms of large scale industrial production. Beyond its value in maintaining a market of the size and continuity needed to support the industry, advertising can cover the failures of research and design. If a module more than 12 feet wide cannot be shipped, make narrow rooms popular.

KEENE CORPORATION

The use of advertising suggests a horizontal direction to corporate growth. And, in fact, the housing factory is also becoming part of large horizontal organizations—e.g., conglomerates. The point of these structures is the protection of the investment. The ability to plan for the total process, the ability to balance the low points of one activity with the highs of another is a corporate version of the ice man who sold coal in the winter. The housing factory is seen as an element of a large system which includes food, clothing, aircraft, communications, and recreation facilities as well as land, appliances, and building materials. This broad view of housing as part of a "shelter industry" moves toward our second scenario.

The first scenario, however, is the housing factory. It has all the elements of what we have come to understand as industrialized building.

(Bottom left) Photo courtesy of Chevrolet Motor Company.

(Bottom right) The marriage of two technologies. (Photo courtesy of Volkswagon.)

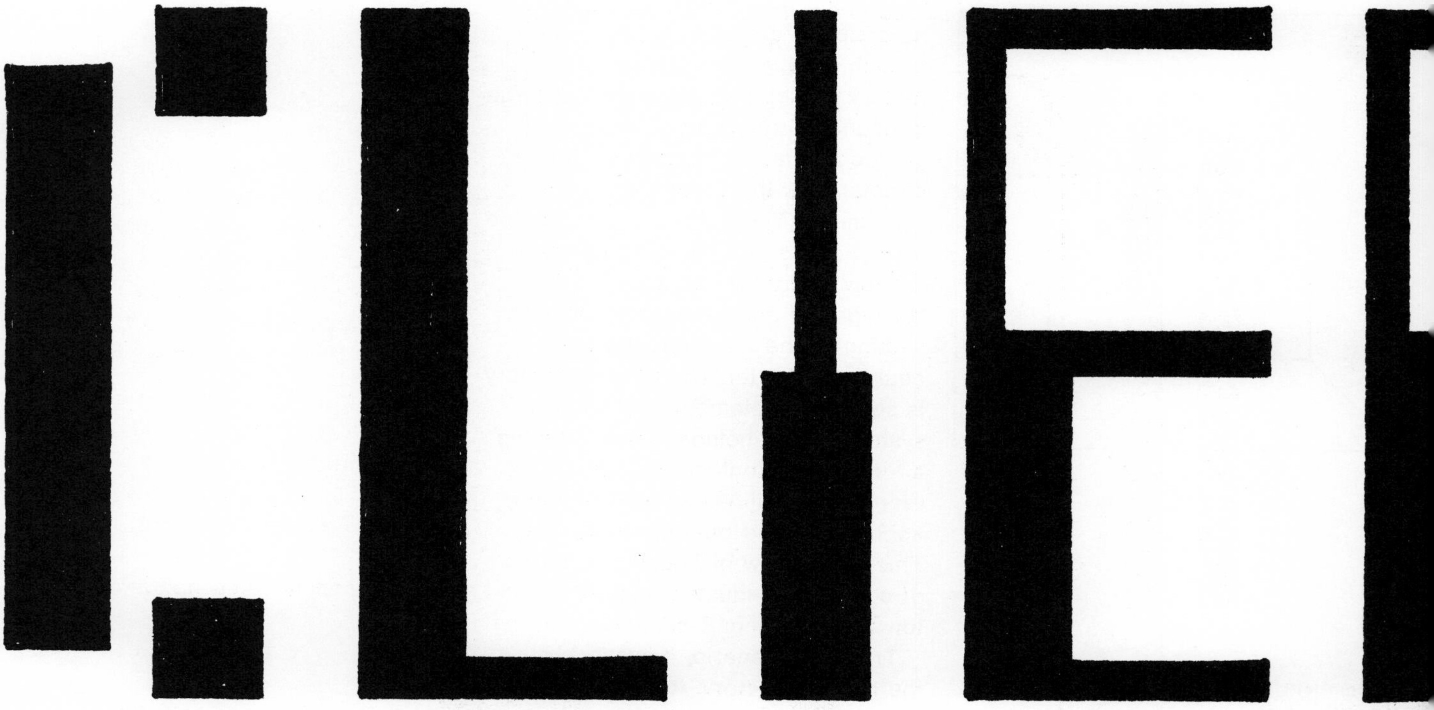

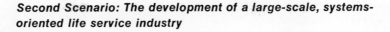

Second Scenario: The development of a large-scale, systems-oriented life service industry

The second scenario is the development of a large-scale, systems-oriented life service industry, which will have charge of all the services, supplies, and systems necessary for the support of community life: public utilities, housing, communication, transportation, and even recreation, education, and medical care. Conglomerates will run each community's system. They will expand vertically, to control the stages from raw material to consumer; and horizontally, to balance the highs and lows of the business cycle.

As part of this process a shelter industry has developed. It views the community, rather than the house, as its product. The basis of this industry is obvious:

Economies of scale will be generated.
Duplication of purchases and inventory can be reduced.
Economies of maintenance—one garage to service the trucks of water, gas, sewer, telephone crews. Multifunction service crews with more compact familiar routes.
Combined building repair, appliance servicing, and building operation.
A single meter reading in a single billing.
The efficiency of combined executive, office, and planning staffs; combined work and service crews.
Broad resources for research, development, and marketing will result.

The list is familiar. It can be found in the textbooks of any business school.
The internal savings generated are paralleled by the savings which will emerge from the consolidation of the many separate government agencies which have been created to deal individually with each of the separate utilities. This can already be seen in the increasing awareness of the "systems" nature of the problems of environment which has led the federal government to combine numbers of agencies into super-agencies. For example, in his "State of the Union" message, January 1971, President Nixon said:

"Over the years we have added departments and created agencies, at the federal level, each to serve a new constituncy or to handle a particular task—and these have grown and multiplied in what has become a hopeless confusion of form and function."
"The time has come to match our structure to our purposes, to look with a fresh eye, and to organize the government by conscious, comprehensive design to meet the new needs of a new era."

In the same message the President proposed combining the existing cabinet organizations into a set of eight new departments: State, Treasury, Justice, Defense, Human Resources, Community Development, Natural Resources, and Economic Development. This move to consolidation parallels a common trend in modern industrial organizations.
Assuming alert management, an industry which controls many difficult functions will soon begin to question the fragmented nature of its activities. We can imagine some scraps of conversations in the board room of the new organization.
"Why do we constantly search for new sources of water, only to overload our sewer and treatment facilities? Perhaps we can reduce the use of potable water as the medium for carrying waste. In this way the total system can be made more economical by increasing the cost of one of its components such as the new waterless toilet or a vacuum sewage system."

"Duplication can be eliminated by selecting the same fuel or energy supply for all the pumps and motors of the system. Waste products can be used as fuel for energy needed in evaporative water treatment processes."

"The recovery of industrial waste particles (such as sulfur from smoke) can be a source of valuable raw materials. Organic waste products can be used as compost for high intensity gardens in a new life cycle."

Once we begin to take this view, countless new arrangements become obvious. The leaders of a new shelter industry will ask:

"Since the bulk of what arrives at each house eventually leaves as solid waste, why can't the truck which makes department store deliveries also remove garbage? Since packaging decisions are part of the solid waste disposal problem, should we consider them together? Can new bicycles be packed in dog food, fertilizer, or fuel?"

One can brainstorm any number of variations.

"Why does the fireman spend so many idle hours while the policeman is overworked? Can't we build prevention as a bigger part of the fireman's job while designing a new multipurpose force? We can have a group of civic employees who inspect buildings and enforce fire laws, while delivering mail, picking up garbage, or patrolling the street. We can devise ways to make them all fire fighters at the necessary time."

The narrow, linear "specialist" view of occupations and services which we have inherited is a convenient *ad hoc* solution to emerging problems. But consider how much more effective our public services could be if we extended this "fireman" view to ambulance service, housing police, building inspection, meter maids, and utility maintenance—as well as to police, fire, garbage, and postal workers.

The core of this scenario is a sort of "General Motors of Communities." The shelter industry will bring a new scale, a new image, and approach to the solution of community problems.

Thus we will begin to define a housing problem in over-all terms of the numbers of people in a community and the activities in which they will engage, rather than the numbers of one, two, and three bedroom apartments needed. In such an analysis, the shelter industry will seek the best "mix," the most efficient combination of living, sleeping, storage, cooking, and sanitary space and public facilities.

When it comes to costs, they will look at the building in terms of real costs rather than capital expenditure. Construction costs alone will be seen to be completely misleading. Maintenance and other annual plan changes, etc., will become costs for heating, repairs, painting, essential to the economy of the organization. The skilled managers of the shelter industry will understand that a two dollar saving each week in operating costs, figured at six percent over twenty years of operation, will free an additional $2,200 of original investment, and their planning will reflect this understanding.

All of the peripheral costs of building will be included: the cost of one piece of land vs. another; the cost of transportation which results from one form of development or density as compared with another; the cost to a community's economy of using land for low density housing, or industry, or agriculture, or as open space. All these will become relevant factors in evaluating one possible development against another.

In looking at these interrelationships within a system, an entirely new picture of the parts may unfold. The traditional approach has been to divide a problem into definite and more manageable subproblems. We separate a city's housing from its traffic, school, and industry location problem. But it will be clear to the shelter industry planners that a change in traffic flows and densities will effect residential patterns, school, and industry concentration. Any one factor is related to the whole problem. In short, what a shelter industry implies is *comprehensive planning,* a large scale systems view which can trace out the effects, "progressive and regressive," of any set of choices and decisions upon all relevant decisions.

This "system" view will make it clear that the problem involves much more than hardware production. Ultimately, it depends upon the techniques of organizing and managing the process itself, and cannot exist where project initiation, design, manufacturing, and marketing are isolated forces. Today the architect views a building as something to design, the carpenter views it as something to work on, the manufacturer as a market for materials, the banker as a source of investment, and the government views it as a source of garbage, sewage, and taxes.

In today's complex society, it is not even possible to separate design decisions from those involving labor relations or foreign policy. To understand and control the nature of our industrialization we must view material production, research, system design, product design, manufacturing, marketing, distribution, and even servicing of the finished product as part of a single operation.

The Princess phone. (Photo of American Telephone & Telegraph Co.)

If it is to be successful, this new, comprehensive organizational structure cannot focus on building products or even buildings. Instead it will consider the total environment as its end product. Again we can begin to see organizational forms which promise to supply the service and support we require without the restrictions and standardization associated with the production of automobiles and appliances. Perhaps General Motors is not the best model. The telephone system may be a better one.

The telephone on your bedside table is not yours. You select its color and style. But unlike the table, which you own, or the wall behind it, which is included in your mortgage, the telephone belongs to the telephone company. The company owns the instrument, the wires, boxes, and controls, those in your house as well as those in the supporting system which links you to telephones all over the world. Because they take this broad responsibility, they have many opportunities to maximize perform- ance. Compare the research activities of the "Bell Labs" with that of the fragmented participants in the building industry. Consider the enormous increase in telephone performance over the past few generations. Compare the ease of arranging for installation or finding telephone repairmen with the problems of changing or repairing home appliances.

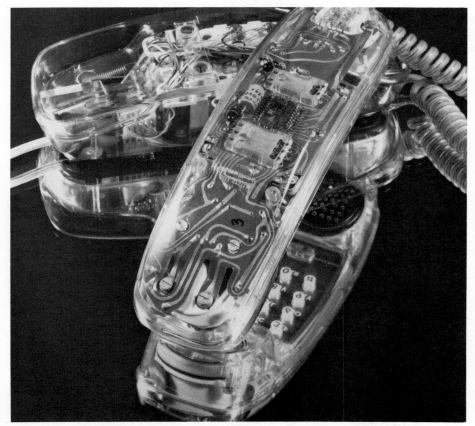

Photo courtesy of Bell Telephone Laboratories.

If you want the best home you can get and don't want to bother with details like where to put it, how to finance it, and who to get to build it, call us.

We take care of everything about your home—from buying the lot, if you need one, to financing and insurance. We arrange it all to fit your budget under the financing plan best suited to you— FHA, VA, Farmers Home Administration or conventional.

Come by or call the Builders Homes office nearest you and let one of our friendly sales counselors show you how easy it will be for you to own your own home.

Builders Homes Inc.

PLAN 120

ALBANY, GA.
5601 Newton Road
just South of the Airport
Albany, Georgia 31702
Phone 912/435-0781

DOTHAN, ALA.
1707 North
Montgomery Highway
Dothan, Ala. 36301
Phone 205/794-2741

MOBILE, ALA.
5464 Government Blvd.
(U.S. 90 Between
I-10 and I-65)
Mobile, Ala. 36600
Phone 205/661-9130

THE PACESETTER

THE WINSLOW

THE BELMONT

Compare the telephone with the electric and plumbing lines which change ownership and responsibility for maintenance at the property line. The utility company provides a pipe to your property. You must take responsibility for its connection. The owner must find individual contractors to do this work. These contractors take a different order of responsibility for their work, and for maintaining and repairing it. We have only to compare the problem and cost of finding a plumber to repair a leaky fixture with that of having a telephone repaired to understand the full force of the change.

Consider these implications in financing a house. All the services and appliances which hook up to houses—pipes, valves, dishwashers, and water heaters—have different life expectancies. Rising expectations and a continuing flow of engineering innovations will make some of these obsolete in only a few years. Other parts may exceed the life of the structure. Yet all are now lumped together as part of the first cost, part of the mortgage. The interest on their cost continues to be paid long after they are replaced.

Perhaps this is a preview of the operation of a shelter industry. We will trade individual choice and personal possessions for the benefits which grow out of comprehensive planning. We will ask larger and larger institutions to take responsibility for solving complex networks of individual problems.

The shelter industry will take a broad responsibility for the structure of communities, in much the same way as builders now develop tracts to support the construction of individual buildings. The new industry will provide cities in which the homeowner can make a variety of personal choices. Just as the telephone company provides a framework which allows us a variety of choices supported by the strengths and resources of the system, the shelter industry will offer support, shelter, and services in a context which can interface with the ability of large industry to produce the components of a community.

Water, electricity, communication, perhaps heating and cooling, as well as the basic structure of the house, will be rented from The Company. The basic cost and responsibility of ownership will be reduced, while services and appliances become rental options. Dishwashers, hot water heaters, and the pipes, lines, and ducts which service them will be part of a single system. They will be part of the capital expense of The Company. The occupant will rent up-to-date, well maintained service. Repairs, replacements, and upgrading of equipment will be functions of one organization. The shelter industry will undertake improvements to maximize the entire system's efficiency. The dishwasher that uses less water will have value in this situation, as will a hot water heater with higher fuel efficiency and lower heat losses. Household appliances will tend to become standardized like the telephone, and become as invisible.

There is a great potential in this scenario. It solves many present problems by applying the advantages of scale and broad control to a fragmented array of activities. It is powerful and logical, but on past performance it is also frightening. What controls will individuals have? What will be the goals of the shelter industry? Will it serve or be served?

One change certainly will be the extension of the concept of a public utility. Isn't housing as much of a public utility as water supply? What about heat, hot water, and air conditioning, as well as power? Can we expect a new level of public control over these aspects of community life? Can we expect more comprehensive planning to ensure real economies. Can we expect that the combination of activities related to specific areas of the community will develop a greater sense of that community and of responsibility to it than is common in the present, fragmented, community systems? Perhaps we should consider a third scenario.

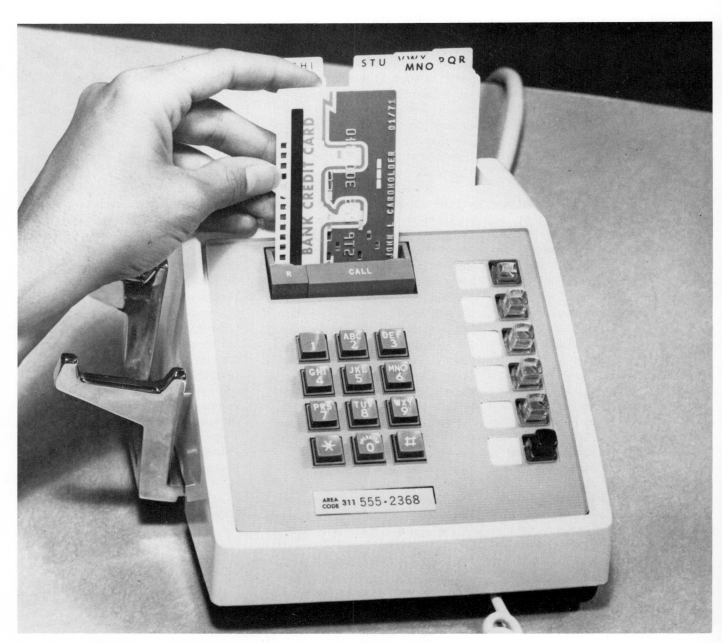

Photo courtesy of Bell Telephone Laboratories.

Third Scenario

We are in the midst of cultural changes which echo a growing discontent with present institutions, and a movement away from them. *The Whole Earth Catalogue* outlines a growing response to this discontent:

> "Remotely done power and glory—as via government, big business, formal education, church—has succeeded to the point where gross defects obscure actual gains. In response to this dilemma and to these gains a realm of intimate personal power is developing—power of the individual to conduct his own education, find his own inspiration, shape his own environment . . ."

This kind of cultural change will inevitably bring about significant changes in technological form and organization. We have discussed recurring concepts which are basic to these changes. One is individuality: the importance of the individual and his relation to technology. A second is the theme of "ephermeralization," the idea of things becoming less permanent, less stable, lighter, thinner, more open, and less structured in a visible way. The third is a movement from linear to dispersed forms. Our third scenario of a future building industry involves all three.

The image in which we view the world is shifting. Conventional thinking is looking at mechanisms linearly, trying to improve and perfect them by extending and improving the lines. This was our first scenario and a good part of the second. But there is another image developing. Young people take it for granted that everything is getting lighter, looser, and more open. Modern music, film, and the underground press are their media of communication rather than the national press. The Volskwagon bus, the camper, motorcycle, transistor radio, tape cassette, and hitchhiking combine to create a mobile, ephemeral, dispersed society, one in which the individual is what is "going on."

"We're not out to manage the old system more efficiently," says Jerry Rubin, "Society will have traveled a full circle, from specialization through industrialization and specialization, back to automation and nonspecialization."

The "crafts" movement based on concepts of individuality, participation, and honesty of product, spurred by dispersal and increased leisure time, is developing a widespread role. Industry's function is the provision of raw materials and tools. Clothing, shoes, furniture, and organic food are currently involved in this trend. Jewelry, pottery, the "Heathkit" radio, auto repairs, and home improvements have been with us for some time. In the future we can expect a major expansion into dwellings, transportation, communication, and even utilities. Our third scenario sees industry's opportunity in reinforcing this trend, rather than in replacing it with a new "mega-industry." The manufacture of transistor radios, tapes and video cassette systems provides a better model for this kind of reinforcement than the restrictive forms of the mobile home industry, new towns, or the TV networks. The new technology and the new life styles call for freedom, mobility, and lack of dependence on a common linear structure.

In this way, power lines can be eliminated by the substitution of total energy systems and single fuel supplies, such as cannisters of gas, used directly for heating, cooling, and the generation of electricity. Solid waste incineration and the re-use of waste heat and energy from household processes promote pressure toward dispersal.

Today we can construct energy storage systems for individual buildings which draw from central supplies at a steady, low level, storing energy for use during short-term peaks. These systems make individual buildings more independent than ever before. There are systems available for resource balancing which are small scale versions of the great regional power grids. These devices link all of a community's resources into a network designed to meet peak demand with shared capacity techniques. They can divert the resources of underused building elements (such as the air conditioning plants and generators of office buildings at night, and schools in summer) to meet the peak demands of homes and public places. In this context the great cities today are starving in the midst of plenty. There is more than enough capacity for the supply of water, energy, and shelter. What is needed are better distribution systems.

Closed water systems can recirculate household water as HVAC systems now do with air. The small amounts of fresh water needed for periodic "topping off" can be supplied by local wells, rainwater precipitation, or truck deliveries. The additional cost of local hardware will be balanced by the savings realized through the elimination of public water systems. These savings can be counted not only in terms of money and space, but in terms of visual and ecological improvement and a vastly increased planning freedom.

Work of this sort has been underway for some time as part of research programs for naval vessels, space vehicles, and aircraft. Large aircraft manufacturers have increased the time required between the removal of toilet wastes from an eight hour cycle to one of hundreds of hours. They use techniques which separate drinking and wash water from waste water, recirculation, solid waste removal, and compaction. The space program has developed systems to sustain life with recirculated fluids for trips of many months. A number of systems which use waste as a source of heat, hot water, or power are already in use.

These closed systems represent more than potential efficiency, they represent the development of a new synthesis. The family unit will have moved from the early freedom of its earth related, closed system of the land, a well, septic tank, compost heap, and fireplace through the linear development of public utilities to a new level of independence and dispersion. High technology products will supply human needs free of the constraints and preconceptions involved in our present view of utilities.

New systems are also emerging for the production of building components which combine the most sophisticated developments of the machine tool industry with new products of the chemical synthesis industry. In this way, materials for building walls can be synthesized with all the qualities of interior and exterior finish, insulation, strength, and weight. Sheets of this material can be worked by numerically controlled machines. Blanks can be cut to exact size, edge conditions can be machined to a wide variety of configurations, openings for windows, doors, pipes, wires, and connections can be cut, drilled, or milled and surface finish and texture can be applied. These operations can be controlled by punched instructions on a paper tape—a truly automated operation. But what is most significant is that each panel can be different from the one before; the machine is not a cookie cutter but a versatile, high-volume, tool.

In this process, as each component is formed a record is made of the exact configuration. Other components in the set are adjusted within a planned set of dimensional tolerances. This record is available in the future if a replacement is required; it can be used to reproduce the exact set of interface configurations with a new texture, finish, or pattern of openings.

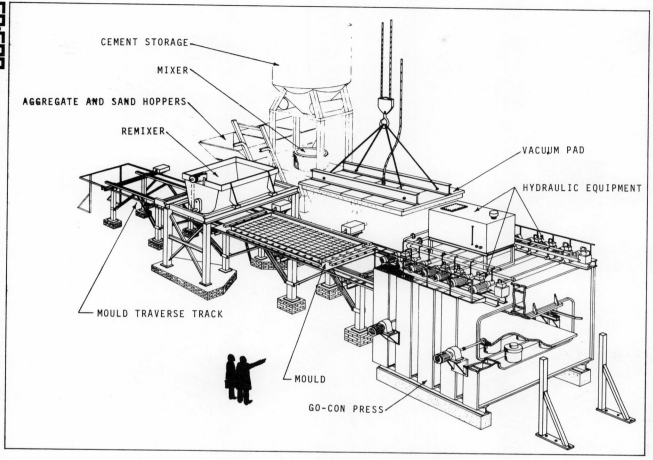

CEMENT STORAGE

MIXER

AGGREGATE AND SAND HOPPERS

REMIXER

VACUUM PAD

HYDRAULIC EQUIPMENT

MOULD TRAVERSE TRACK

MOULD

GO-CON PRESS

GO·CON press kit material

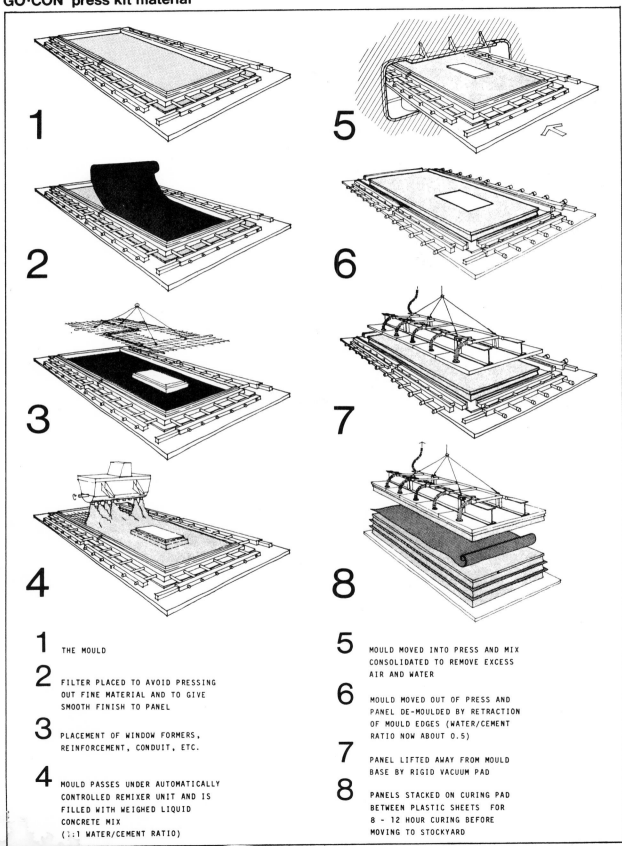

1 THE MOULD

2 FILTER PLACED TO AVOID PRESSING OUT FINE MATERIAL AND TO GIVE SMOOTH FINISH TO PANEL

3 PLACEMENT OF WINDOW FORMERS, REINFORCEMENT, CONDUIT, ETC.

4 MOULD PASSES UNDER AUTOMATICALLY CONTROLLED REMIXER UNIT AND IS FILLED WITH WEIGHED LIQUID CONCRETE MIX (1:1 WATER/CEMENT RATIO)

5 MOULD MOVED INTO PRESS AND MIX CONSOLIDATED TO REMOVE EXCESS AIR AND WATER

6 MOULD MOVED OUT OF PRESS AND PANEL DE-MOULDED BY RETRACTION OF MOULD EDGES (WATER/CEMENT RATIO NOW ABOUT 0.5)

7 PANEL LIFTED AWAY FROM MOULD BASE BY RIGID VACUUM PAD

8 PANELS STACKED ON CURING PAD BETWEEN PLASTIC SHEETS FOR 8 - 12 HOUR CURING BEFORE MOVING TO STOCKYARD

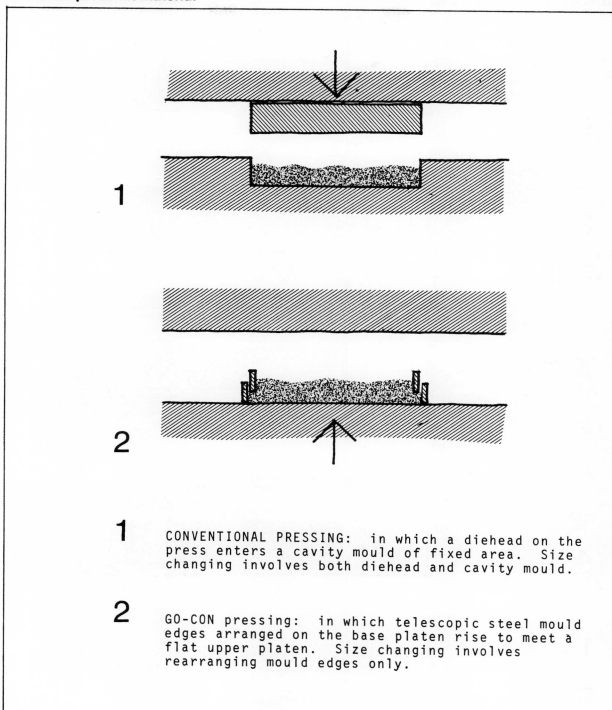

1 CONVENTIONAL PRESSING: in which a diehead on the press enters a cavity mould of fixed area. Size changing involves both diehead and cavity mould.

2 GO-CON pressing: in which telescopic steel mould edges arranged on the base platen rise to meet a flat upper platen. Size changing involves rearranging mould edges only.

GO·CON

GO·CON press kit material

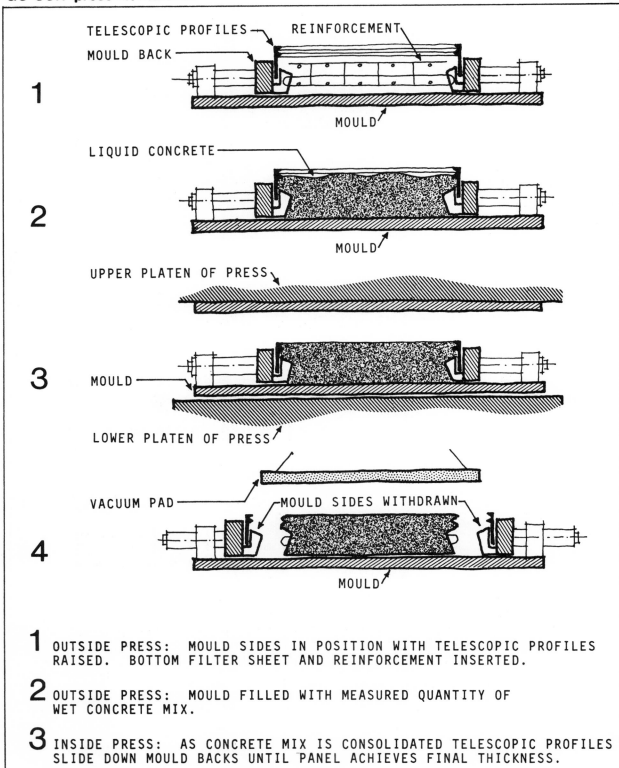

TELESCOPIC PROFILES
REINFORCEMENT
MOULD BACK

1 MOULD

LIQUID CONCRETE

2 MOULD

UPPER PLATEN OF PRESS

3 MOULD

LOWER PLATEN OF PRESS

VACUUM PAD

MOULD SIDES WITHDRAWN

4 MOULD

1 OUTSIDE PRESS: MOULD SIDES IN POSITION WITH TELESCOPIC PROFILES RAISED. BOTTOM FILTER SHEET AND REINFORCEMENT INSERTED.

2 OUTSIDE PRESS: MOULD FILLED WITH MEASURED QUANTITY OF WET CONCRETE MIX.

3 INSIDE PRESS: AS CONCRETE MIX IS CONSOLIDATED TELESCOPIC PROFILES SLIDE DOWN MOULD BACKS UNTIL PANEL ACHIEVES FINAL THICKNESS.

4 OUTSIDE PRESS: MOULD SIDES ARE WITHDRAWN AND CONSOLIDATED PANEL IS LIFTED AWAY BY RIGID VACUUM PAD. PROFILES ARE RAISED AND MOULD SIDES ARE RE-POSITIONED FOR NEXT PRESSING.

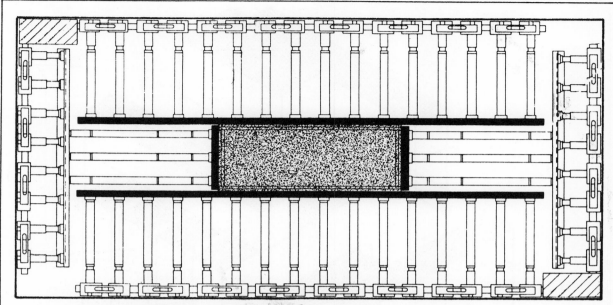

Mould set for small panel 2490 mm x 920 mm

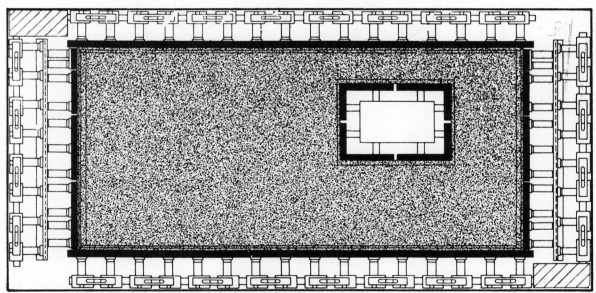

Mould set for large panel 6100 mm x 2810 mm with window insert

ADJUSTABLE MOULD

THESE DIAGRAMS SHOW THE PRINCIPLE OF THE METHOD USED
TO ALTER MOULD SIZES AND CONFIGURATION. THE TOP DIAGRAM
SHOWS HOW SPACER TUBES ARE USED BETWEEN THE MOULD SIDES
AND THE MECHANICAL DE-MOULDING GEAR WHICH IS PERMANENTLY
SITUATED AT THE PERIMETER OF THE MOULD. THE BOTTOM DIA-
GRAM SHOWS THE LARGEST PANEL THAT CAN BE MADE, REQUIRING
NO SPACER TUBES.

GO·CON

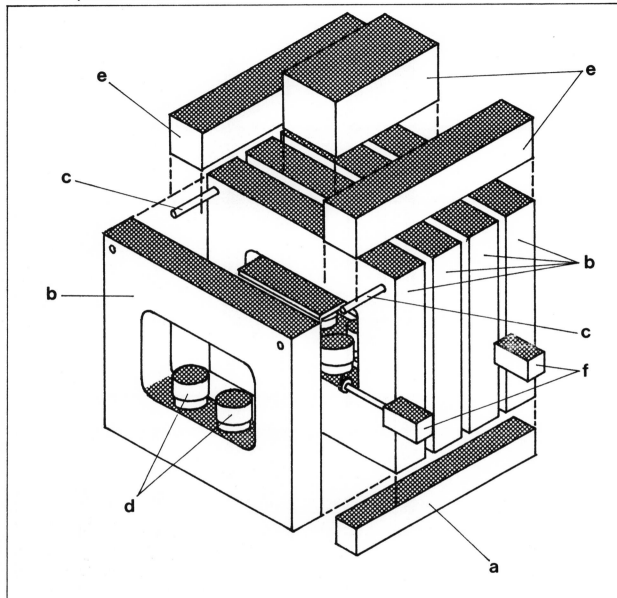

BASIC CONSTRUCTION OF THE GO-CON PRESS

a FOUNDATIONS TO WHICH FRAMES ARE FIXED

b FABRICATED HOLLOW RING FRAMES

c LONG BOLTS CONNECTING FRAMES AT TOP

d MAIN DRIVE HYDRAULIC CYLINDERS (2 PER FRAME)

e HYDRAULIC SYSTEM MOUNTED ON TOP OF PRESS

f MOTORS FOR TRAVERSING MOULD INTO AND OUT OF PRESS

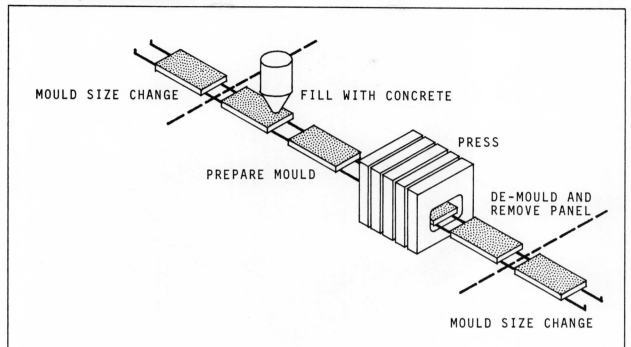

MOULD SIZE CHANGE   FILL WITH CONCRETE

PREPARE MOULD

PRESS

DE-MOULD AND REMOVE PANEL

MOULD SIZE CHANGE

PRODUCTION SYSTEMS: "ONE PLUS ONE"

THIS IS PROBABLY THE SIMPLEST PRACTICAL SYSTEM. A SINGLE
MOULD IS USED IN THE PRODUCTION CYCLE, PLUS ONE OTHER
MOULD WHICH CAN BE SET UP FOR THE NEXT PANEL TYPE REQUIRED
IN ONE OF THE SIZE CHANGE STATIONS AT EITHER END OF THE
TRACK. IN THIS WAY PRODUCTION IS NOT INTERRUPTED BETWEEN
PANEL TYPES.

PLANNED PRESS CYCLE TIME	=	15 MINUTES
OUTPUT PER HOUR	=	4 PRESSINGS
OUTPUT PER 40 HOUR SHIFT	=	160 PRESSINGS
UTILISATION OF PRESS	=	20%
ANNUAL OUTPUT OF PLANT WORKING 2 SHIFTS	=	10,976 PANELS

THIS OUTPUT REPRESENTS ABOUT 500 DWELLING UNITS

GO·CON

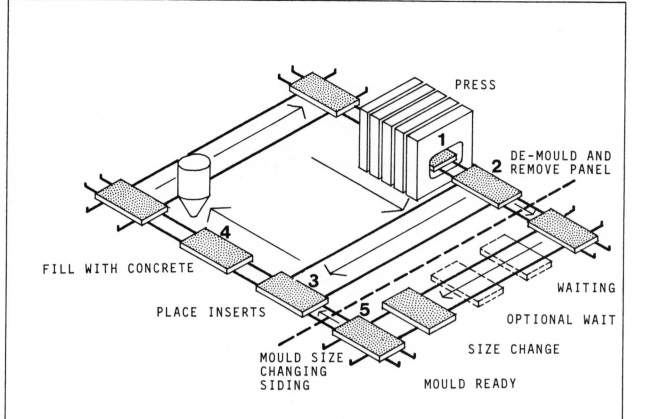

PRESS

1

2 DE-MOULD AND
   REMOVE PANEL

WAITING

OPTIONAL WAIT

SIZE CHANGE

4

FILL WITH CONCRETE

PLACE INSERTS

3

5

MOULD SIZE
CHANGING
SIDING

MOULD READY

PRODUCTION SYSTEMS: "FOUR PLUS ONE"

THIS IS THE PREFERRED SYSTEM FOR OPTIMUM PRACTICAL UTILI-
SATION OF THE PRESS. FOUR MOULDS (POSITIONS INDICATED BY
NUMBERS 1, 2, 3, 4) TRAVEL ON A "MERRY-GO-ROUND" TRACK
BETWEEN STATIONS AT WHICH VARIOUS OPERATIONS ARE CARRIED
OUT. A FIFTH MOULD IS PREPARED IN A SIZE CHANGE "SIDING"
DURING PRODUCTION. AS SOON AS ONE OF THE FOUR MOULDS IN
THE CIRCUIT HAS COMPLETED ITS BATCH OF PANELS IT ENTERS
THE SIDING AND THE FIFTH MOULD, SET UP TO MAKE THE NEXT
PANEL TYPE, IS INTRODUCED TO THE CIRCUIT. IN THIS WAY
PRODUCTION IS NOT INTERRUPTED BETWEEN PANEL TYPES.

PLANNED PRESS CYCLE TIME   =   4 MINUTES

OUTPUT PER HOUR   =   15 PRESSINGS

OUTPUT PER 40 HOUR SHIFT   =   600 PRESSINGS

UTILISATION OF PRESS   =   73% . . . .

ANNUAL OUTPUT OF PLANT
WORKING 2 SHIFTS   =   41,160 PANELS

THIS OUTPUT REPRESENTS ABOUT 2,000 DWELLING UNITS

In the foreground is the mould set to make a 20 ft x 9 ft x 5 in. panel. The hydraulic equipment mounted on top of the press can be clearly seen. (Photo courtesy of Go-Con Concrete Ltd., England.)

The rigid vacuum pad about to lower a panel onto the curing pad. Adhesion to the pad is prevented by placing a polythene sheet between the pad and the panel. Control cabin can be seen in background. (Photo courtesy of Go-Con Concrete Ltd., England.)

Photo courtesy of the American Plywood Association.

Future developments in this direction will see housing factories making tools and pieces rather than finished houses. These tools will be designed to make people less dependent on decisions made remotely at a factory or planning office. We are inventing a kind of "automated cottage industry" where homemaking is meant to be part of daily life. The home is expected to grow, change, and perhaps to move with each family. This is a scenario in which dwelling takes its original meaning: as a verb, not a noun. It conflicts dramatically with the image of a house factory. Existing factories are designed to produce ready-to-wear houses in a world that is ready for custom tailoring.

The utilities, services, and subdivisions we provide to support these houses are equally out of step. When technology is turned around to the point where we give people tools, the mechanism, and a design framework which will support them, the dwelling will become the creation of its user, rather than a response to the needs of technology.

Are existing industries capable of using these new tools? Can they turn their energies from an involvement in metropolitan scale power generation and its related problems of air and thermal pollution, oil spills, blackouts, congestion, and inflexibility. Can they ignore construction of thirty-million gallons per day desalinization plants and even larger canals and reservoirs? Can they begin to concentrate on the new dispersed package?

Experience indicates that they cannot.

Just as the railroads could not move into the emerging automobile industry, the telephone companies did not enter radio, the photographic establishment did not discover Polaroid photography or dry copying, and the electronics industry ignored computers; this scenario pictures established industries slowly dying to be replaced by new industries which emerge to meet new needs.

Application of the Principles of Systems Integration to the Design of the Nursing Tower Portion of a VA Hospital Facility (Phase 2)   Project 99·R042

Ducker's Portable Barrack and Field Hospital. (Published in 1886.)

Volume Two   DESIGN   MANUAL

163

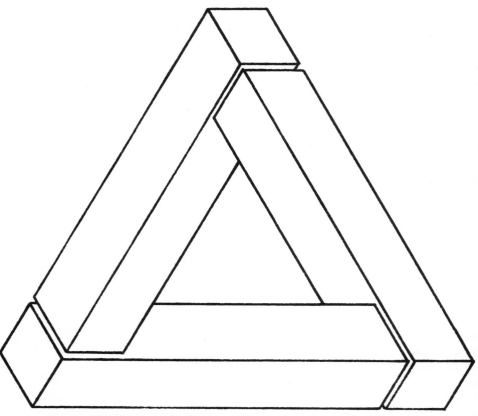

Photo courtesy of Chevrolet Motor Company.

We have seen that much of the problem of industrializing the building industry has grown out of the mistaken image of the automobile industry as a model; a view which focuses on the house and the housing project as products and the factory as a tool for making them. But the house as a manufactured product and the factory as a tool for house making are concepts in conflict with real forces and desires in the community. Individuality, choice, change, continued life and growth of dwellings come in conflict with the need to plan, order, and make situations secure. The manufactured-house industry, from on-site factories to mobile homes, has struggled against a fierce wall of consumer resistance. Each year, more consumers are forced to accept these products out of desperate need, enormous media pressure, and the overwhelming weight of government applied through subsidy, tax relief, loans, mortgage insurance, codes, sewer, and water grants, and a host of other powerful weapons.

It has been building's Vietnam. All the force of our nation cannot seem to make it work. No conceivable escalation of resources committed seems to help. Perhaps our image is wrong, and we can go at the problem in another way.

This scenario does not suggest a retreat from industrialization. It simply calls for another model: a "Sears Roebuck" of housing; a new building industry that would be responsible for the manufacture and distribution of components rather than finished houses. The critical function of this new industry would be the operation of an information and distribution system.

The new organization would have a broad information system relating to manufactured products available from the inventory of many manufacturers. It would consider delivery time, interface configuration, and the skills needed for installation, as well as the more conventional characteristics of size, shape, weight, and finish.

The service would be introduced to the public through a network of distribution centers around the country: "Building Centers." To use the service, the customer, either an individual or a building organization, would bring his plans or sketches to the Building Center. At the Center, the plans would be scanned, required components identified, a schedule established and matched against information relating to cost availability and product performance. A print-out would provide minor dimensional adjustments. It would also give accurate cost estimates, a schedule of the work, and indicate those components which conflict with stated goals (time, budget, or compliance with a specific program).

The Building Center would take responsibility for assembling all of the components, packing them in containers so that they can be removed in order as they are needed, and shipping on a schedule which parallels that of the overall construction. For the builder many problems would be solved. He would deal with a single source of contact. Losses, weather damage, and pilferage are reduced by the container, costs are more predictable, and scheduling more sophisticated than individual contractors can now manage. The contractor would no longer deal with individual suppliers in ignorance and without the leverage of large-scale buying. He would be supported by a sophisticated planning, scheduling, inventory, and credit system which would increase his effectiveness.

The user has a better opportunity to work with or to be his own builder. The new organization is a service to help building develop along diverse lines. It is directed toward the support of the individual and the small builder rather than at replacing him.

We can recognize the beginnings of these activities in some aspects of today's building industry. Lumber yards now approach this service in an unsophisticated, carpentry-trade oriented fashion. Precut houses use the package but eliminate most of the owner's choice. Some major companies are experimenting with planning, inventory control, scheduling, and containerization of the sort which has previously been the special competence of the aircraft industry.

Another aspect of large-scale manufacturing operations, the "make-or-buy" decision, will play a significant part in operations of this new building organization. Aircraft manufacturers assemble many thousands of components into each air frame. These are manufactured by large and small organizations all over the world. The airplane builder is much closer to today's building general contractor than most of us realize. For each component, performance is specified, as is the interface configuration. Bids are requested. Where the bid price or time of delivery seems excessive, the company goes through a "make-or-buy" decision. They decide whether they should buy or manufacture the product themselves.

At the warehouses where packaging and containerization take place components can be assembled into subassemblies rather than packaged as separate pieces. New products would suggest themselves to the managers of the Center as well as ways to improve old ones.

The Center, seeing major weaknesses in traditional products such as separate bath, toilet, and sink fixtures, would prepare performance requirements for a new approach to bath fixtures or closets or doors or walls. Manufacturers would develop products to meet these requirements. The prize is a large guaranteed market.

In this way, a new industry could develop which serves and supports builders and maximizes choice. Sears is one model, the *Whole Earth Catalogue* may be a better one. Both approaches help us to look at more and more of a building as components, as furniture and tools, rather than as a complete house.

This extended view of what constitutes furniture is another significant point of departure. What should be considered furniture, and in what framework shall it be arranged? Where are the boundaries that should be drawn between the public and the individual? Are there some activities which are the right and responsibility of the community, and others which are in the province of individuals and groups? Can we devise a structure in which this decomposition can easily be made?

The outlines of such separation appear if we consider a bookcase and its relationship to the things it holds. Here we may find clues to a method of using industry and the individual in a new symbiosis. Let us compare the bookcase to the housing project.

Would not bookcase production be better planned if we insisted that each person buy his bookcase with books in it? In this way the factory could take advantage of large scale planning, bulk purchasing, simplified packing, shipping, and a single marketing organization. Consultants could be hired to help select the best, most important, most beautiful books. Municipal codes could decide which books are healthy for us. They could list the ones we must have and protect us from books which are unhealthy. No longer would one have to buy a bookcase and then go through the bother of separately buying the books and arranging them in it. The whole thing would be assembled in the factory and sold as a package. Soon, as indicated in our second scenario, bookcase manufacturers will enter the publishing field as well as the lumber, paint, and transportation businesses.

Isn't this what is happening in the housing factory? We say: "You have a choice of standard variations. You can have a classical bookcase, a mystery bookcase, or a bookcase with a few knick-knacks in it. But the idea of making your own mixture of classical and mystery or knick-knacks is something which is just too difficult for the industrial process to handle. It is too expensive, too special—you simply cannot afford it."

The bookcase analogy translated to the housing project provides another image. The community's responsibility to housing could be the provision of a framework very much like a bookcase. In it individuals could make their own dwellings much as they arrange books and knick-knacks in a bookcase.

This new separation between public and private, between frames and components, is particularly interesting in terms of the numbers necessary for effective industrial production and their match with the individuality that consumers demand.

There are many different systems which can compose the building frame or structure. Many of these are called building systems but most of them are simply structural systems. They are made of wood, steel, concrete, and plastic. But a universal denominator among them is the fact that if one is to provide about 1000 dwellings a year, and can guarantee production for three, four, or five years, he has enough of a basic market to build a factory. If the kind of equipment and facilities we have begun to believe we need are added, there are other sets of numbers to consider. 5000 families may have to be aggregated before a window manufacturer can make a particular window. 25,000 customers are required before an air-conditioner manufacturer can make a new unit and 50,000 or 100,000 before General Electric will change the door swing on a refrigerator. Two hundred million of us have to be hooked into a standardized telephone system to make it effective.

These are particular numbers. There is an optimal point in the production of each component. This differs, depending on the scale of the component, the tools required, shipping, marketing, and usage.

168 Mobile home interior. (Photos courtesy of Ramada Homes, Division of Skyline Corp.)

The building frame, the subsystem which is most closely related to the ground, and the special conditions of earth, contour, and climate requires the smallest market for efficient production. As you move to windows, air conditioners and refrigerators, increasingly larger numbers of people are needed to form a basic market for products which are unrelated to particular places.

These numbers tell us that we can begin to structure a mass production industry on different levels. They tell us that we can build 25 different frame systems ("bookcases"), for every air conditioner; that we can make 100 different support systems for every variation in refrigerator. We can begin to see a variety of building types emerge with many more possibilities for individual frameworks, spaces, and arrangements than for appliances and parts.

A number of frameworks for dwelling, which are planned to be finished by the individual much as he now arranges his furniture within a room, are possible. Each of us can have a Danish Modern or a French Provincial apartment, a great deal of furniture or very little. We can select our own color schemes and fabrics and move furniture, fittings, walls, and rooms to meet our own needs from day to day or hire others to do it for us. We can do all of these things within the framework of our present technical capacity, supported by, rather than controlled by, industrial production.

Townland, one of the original Breakthrough winners, has since dropped out of the project, but the concept of treating the structural framework as "land in the air" is one of the most interesting concepts to come out of the project. These sketches show a concept for such a framework, its street (utilities move horizontally under the street), its backyards, and their variety of housing and related functions which the structure can accommodate.

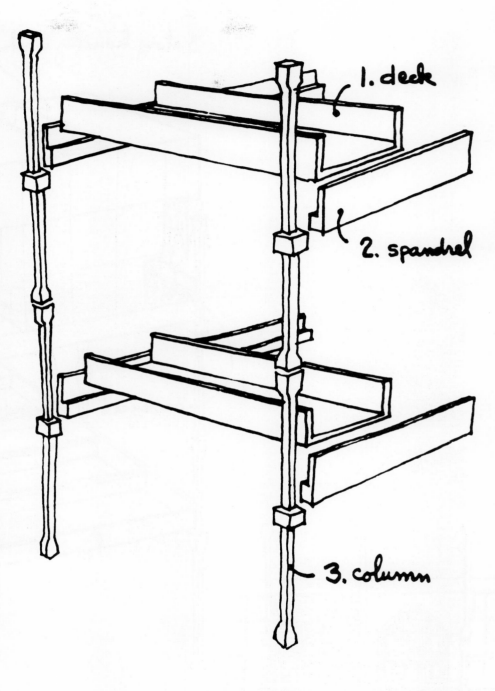

1. deck

2. spandrel

3. column

Subsystem 1
Precast Structural Members

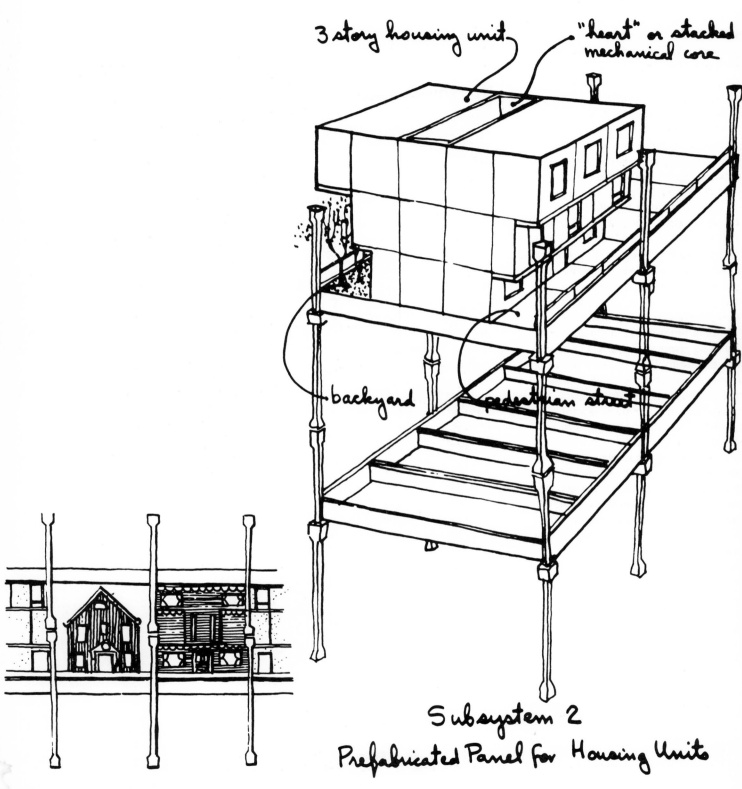

3 story housing unit

"heart" or stacked mechanical core

backyard

pedestrian street

Subsystem 2
Prefabricated Panel for Housing Units

Frameworks such as Townland's are no more restrictive than the street lot zoning system of most two dimensional concepts. Any sort of house and construction technology is possible.

Townland suggests a new interface between public and private, community and home. The infill lends itself to the mass production of components, and the framework to limited production closely linked to local conditions and customs.

Most of today's furniture is factory made. It can be examined in department stores and showrooms, delivered, charged or financed. It combines easily with other elements of the household and is supported by floors, walls, or ceilings. A manufacturer knows what size to make mattresses, because there are generally accepted industry standards for beds, sheets, blankets, spreads, blanket covers, pillows, and pillow cases. Industrial production works very well in this area and does it with little restriction on variety.

Our look at factory-made bookcases and factory made rooms suggests that we should begin to question some of the axioms of the architectural and planning professions.

This scenario requires only a shift of image. We can see the framework in a typical builder's tract. The tract is a one-level bookcase. The builder makes raw land useful. He adds roads, utilities, and drainage and partitions building lots. A framework in the sky can do the same thing in three dimensions by making it possible for people to have space in the framework and design their own houses. Modern office buildings provide this opportunity as do "loft" spaces and expensive cooperative housing.

Within this framework, a family can make its own house, have someone build it for them, or move mobiles, modules, or components into the framework. Groups of people can get together and buy a large space for apartments or a commune. Developers can build houses, as can a local Housing Authority and a variety of nonprofit organizations: church groups, pension funds, and building societies. Other services related to housing can fit the framework, schools or shops, parking, a restaurant, libraries, clubrooms, workshops, and medical services. The framework, like the bookcase, is a mechanism to support activity. It is unconcerned whether it holds Shakespeare, mysteries, medical, or school books.

We are just beginning to understand these frameworks. Their potential for richness and variety remains unexplored, and their design poses one of the greatest challenges for the next generation of architects.

A VIEW OF THE FUTURE   We have had a view of the future: we are not going "back to nature," nor must we accept the factory made house. There is a new symbiosis, a new combination of man and technology, that is creating dwelling instead of housing.

The industry which will serve our building needs must have many facets. It must be an industry loosely linked through visible and invisible networks of information and interdependence. Participants must manufacture and use products of many kinds and scales ranging from hinges, bolts, and locks to finished rooms and houses. The products of this diverse manufacture must be tied together by a widely understood and respected framework. The new industry will support the production of a wide range of components and a medium in which they can be brought together to make successful communities.

These are our scenarios: the development of a factory-built house industry, a large-scale systems-oriented shelter industry, and the emergence of a new individual-oriented, dispersed, "Whole Earth Catalogue" of tools and materials.

In the last third of the twentieth century, we have come to believe that technology can solve our problems. It holds the promise of conquering poverty, providing health, happiness, peaceful, and productive lives for all of the world's population. We have also learned that it poses enormous threats. It can divert our resources and feed itself at the expense of human needs, or it can wipe out all of humanity in one enormous catastrophe. Technology today is at the center of our experience and perception. Concern for the individual within a systematic technological context must replace technology in that center. We must recognize that the institutions with which we manage technology are the narrow linear products of an earlier technology. They lack the richness and vitality which are now possible.

The planning of human shelter is no longer a simple matter. The complexity of our society and tremendous advances in science not only permit, but require, man's shelter to be much more than protection against the elements. It must satisfy his economic, social, and psychological needs as well.

It is time we stopped deluding ourselves with over-simplification and understatement about the meaning of the new technology. The changes in our technical vocabulary point to far more than the opportunity to do what we are used to doing faster, cheaper, or better. The supersonic jet is not simply a high velocity substitute for the horse; the electronic computer is much more than a device for calculating quickly; and the new housing unit will be much more than just another house on the street. These innovations are changing our world, our institutions, and our way of working. To understand this new world is the central problem of our time.

We have viewed three scenarios. Which will it be?

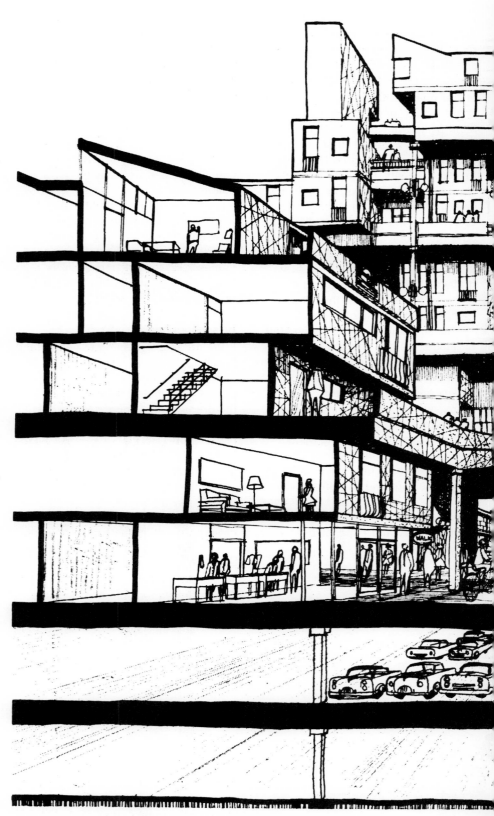

Townland's Breakthrough proposal.

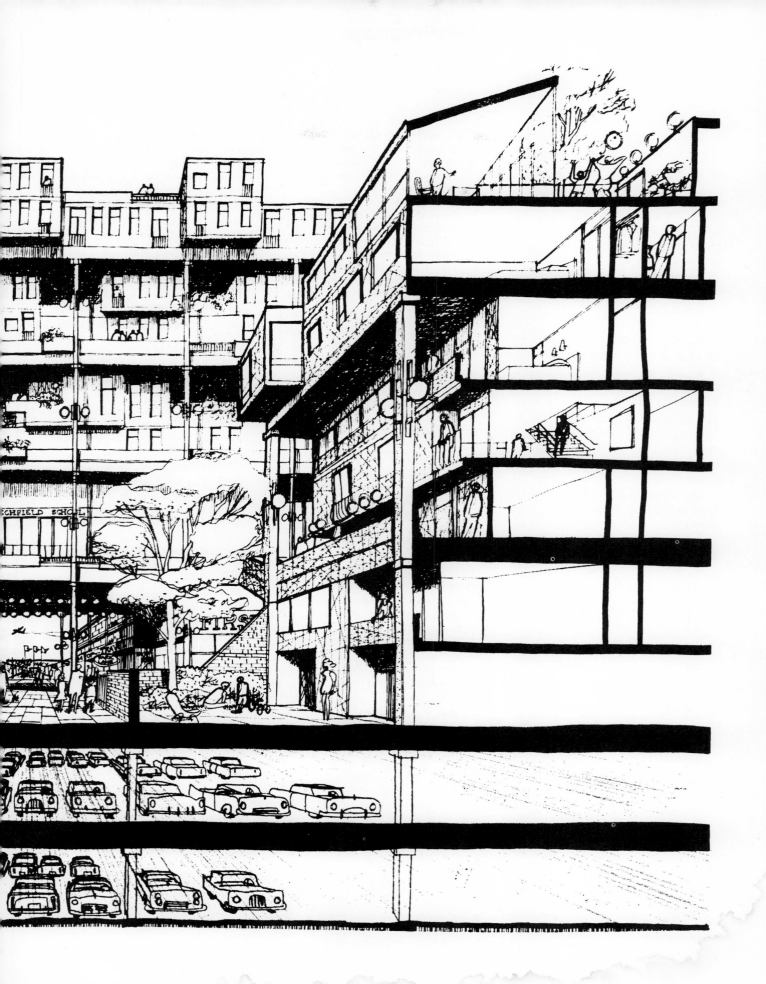

bibliography

The books on the list which follows cover a broad range of subjects, related to Industry and Technology. To help the reader find his way, the following key is offered:

A General view of industry and technology.
B General view of industry and technology in building.
C Survey of a broad group of systems materials or methods.
D Survey of a specific category of systems, materials, or methods.
E Studies of particular projects, systems or methods.
F History.

The letter key after each item identifies its principle areas of concern.

Bemis, Albert Farwell, *The Evolving House,* The Technology Press, MIT 1936. (B,C,F)

Bender, Richard, *Selected Aspects of the American Building Industry: The Industrialization of Building:* A Report to the National Commission on Urban Problems, 1968. (B,C)

Boice, John R., *A History and Evaluation of SCSD, Building Systems,* Information Clearing House, Menlo Park, California. (E)

Burke, John G. (ed.), *The New Technology and Human Values,* Wadsworth, Belmont, California, 1968. (A,F)

Center for Housing and Environmental Studies, *The New Building Block,* Cornell University, 1968. (B,D)

Crane, David A., *Developing New Communities, Application of Technical Innovations,* Washington, U. S. Department of Housing and Urban Development, 1970. (D,E)

Diament, R. M. E., *Industrialized Building,* Three volumes, ILIFFE Books, Ltd., London, 1964. (C)

Drucker, Peter, *The Age of Discontinuity,* Harper & Row, 1969 (A)

————, *Technology, Management and Society,* Harper & Row, 1970 (A).

Education Facilities Laboratories, SCSD: *The Project and the Schools,* EFL, New York, 1967. (E)

Fitch, James M., *American Building, The Historical Forces That Shape It,* Houghton Mifflin, 1966. (A,B,F)

Galbraith, John K., *The New Industrial State,* Houghton Mifflin Co., 1967. (A)

Gidieon, Sigfried, *Mechanization Takes Command,* Oxford, 1948. (A,F)

Habraken, N.J., *Supports: An Alternative to Mass Housing,* The Architectural Press, London, 1972. (E)

Hardless, Trevor (ed), *Europofab Systems Handbook, Housing,* Interbuild Publications, London, 1969. (C)

House and Home, *The New Housing Industry,* reprint of an 8-part series, 1964, (B,D).

International Council for Building Research, *Innovation in Building,* Elsevier, Amsterdam, 1962. (B)

————. *Towards Industrialized Building,* Elsevier, Amsterdam, 1966. (B)

Koch, Carl and Lewis, Roger K., *Roadblocks to Innovation in the Housing Industry,* A Report to the National Commission on Urban Problems, 1968, (B,D,F)

Kelly, Burnham, *The Prefabrication of Houses,* The Technology Press, MIT, 1951. (B,C)

————, and Associates, *Design and the Production of Houses,* McGraw-Hill, 1959. (B)

McLuhan, Herbert Marshall, Understanding Media. *The Extensions of Man,* McGraw-Hill, 1964. (A)

Malmstrom, P. E. & Munch-Petersen, J. C., *Philosophy of Design of Industrialized Housing,* U.N. Social and Economic Council ST/ELLA/CONF. (27/L.5), 1967. (B,E)

Reidelbach, J.A., *Modular Housing,* MODCO, Inc. Annendale, Virginia, 1970. (B,D)

The Report of the National Commission on Urban Problems (The Douglas Commission), *Building the American City,* 1969. (B)

The Report of the President's Committee on Urban Housing (The Kaiser Committee), *A Decent Home,* 1968. (B)

Safdie, Moshe, *Beyond Habitat,* MIT Press, 1970. (B,E)

Schon, Donald, *Technology and Change,* Delacorte, 1967. (A)

———, *Loss of the Stable State,* Random House, 1971 (A)

Sebestyen, Gyula, *Large Panel Buildings,* Akademia Kiado, Budapest, 1965. (D)

Stonebraker, Gary K. and Building Systems Development, Inc., *The Impact of Social and Technical Change in Building,* U.S. Department of Commerce, Commerce Clearing House, 1967. (B)

Testa, Carlo & Schmiid, Thomas, *Systems Building:* an International Survey of Methods, Praeger, 1969. (B,D)

U.S. Department of Commerce, National Bureau of Standards, *Industrialized Building in the Soviet Union,* NBS Special Publications #334, May 1972. (D,E)

U.S. Department of Housing and Urban Development, Division of International Affairs, Special Report, Industrialized Building: *A Comparative Analysis of European Experience,* B. P. O. 1968. (B,D)

U. S. Department of Housing and Urban Development, *Housing Systems Proposals for Operation Breakthrough,* Government Printing Office, Washington, D.C. 1971. (C,E)

U. S. Department of Housing and Urban Development and MITRE, *An Analysis of Twelve Experimental Housing Projects,* U. S. Government Printing Office, ST/MI, 1966. (D,E)

Walker, Charles R. (ed), *Technology, Industry and Man in the Age of Acceleration,* McGraw-Hill, 1968. (A)

PERIODICALS

There are a number of periodicals which report on developments in the building industry. The following list is keyed to identify publications with:

A. General architectural interest
B. An engineering and construction interest
C. A special interest in the production of housing.
D. A special interest in building systems.
E. A detailed coverage of current tools, techniques and materials for building.

Note: Current work and research of the various departments and organizations of the U. S. Federal Government are often published and distributed through: U. S. Department of Commerce, National Technical Information Service, Springfield, Virginia, 22151. Superintendent of Documents, U. S. Government Printing Office, Washington, D. C. Both of these organizations publish regular announcements of new publications.

Architectural Design, The Standard Catalogue Co., Ltd., London (A)

Architectural Forum, Whitney Publications, Inc. New York (A)

Architectural Record, McGraw-Hill, New York, New York (A)

Automation in Housing, Vance Publishing Co., Chicago, Ill, (C,E)

Building Design and Construction, Cahners Publishing Co., Chicago, Ill. (C,D,E)

Engineering News Record, McGraw-Hill, New York (B,E)

House & Home, McGraw-Hill, New York, New York (C,E)

Industrialized Building, Building and Contracts Journal, Ltd. London (D,E)

Interbuild, Prefabrication Publications, Ltd. London (C,D)

Progressive Architecture, Reinhold Publishing Co., Stamford, Conn. (A)

Systems Building, W.R.C. Smith Publishing Co., Atlanta, Ga. (D,E)

The Whole Earth Catalogue (Access to Tools), Portola Institute, Menlo Park, California.

index